KU-334-795

Report 130   1993

Methane: its occurrence and hazards in construction

P J Hooker MA, PhD, C Geol, FGS
M P Bannon BSc, PhD

D
622.8
HOO

BRITISH GEOLOGICAL SURVEY, Kingsley Dunham
Centre, Keyworth, Nottingham, United Kingdom NG12 5GG
Tel: 0602 363100   Telex: 378173 BGSKEY G   Fax: 0602 363200

CONSTRUCTION INDUSTRY RESEARCH AND INFORMATION ASSOCIATION
6 Storey's Gate, Westminster, London SW1P 3AU
Tel 071-222 8891   Fax 071-222 1708

Summary

Methane and other gases often present with it, whether naturally occurring or in landfill gas, are dangerous. Throughout the construction process and the subsequent operation of the finished works, situations can arise of hazard to people and property. This Report provides guidance for construction professionals who may have to take these gases into account. After a summary of the physical and chemical properties of these gases, their hazardous characteristics are explained. How and in what situations methane is formed, how it moves or can be moved in the ground, and how the source of the methane can be identified are explained. Case histories and scenarios of typical situations are used to show how and where methane can affect construction projects. The Report and its appendices provide information which will enable construction professionals to recognise potential methane problems and to initiate the process of finding solutions for them. Engineering solutions, however, are not put forward as these are the subject of subsequent CIRIA projects.

P J Hooker MA PhD C Geol, FGS
M P Bannon BSc PhD
Methane: its occurrence and hazards in construction
Construction Industry Research and Information Association
CIRIA Report 130 1993

Keywords:
Methane, landfill gas, origins, properties, hazards, construction situations

Reader Interest:
Construction and environmental professionals, developers, planners

All rights reserved. No part of this publication may be reproduced or transmitted in any form or by any means, including photocopying and recording, without the written permission of the copyright holder, application for which should be addressed to the publisher. Such written permission must also be obtained before any part of this publication is stored in a retrieval system of any nature.

ISBN 0 86017 373 9

ISSN 0305 408X

© CIRIA 1993

CLASSIFICATION	
AVAILABILITY	Unrestricted
CONTENT	Technical guidance
STATUS	Committee guided
USER	Construction professionals

Published by CIRIA, 6 Storey's Gate Westminster London SW1P 3AU

UNIVERSITY OF STRATHCLYDE

30125 00447302 0

ANDERSONIAN LIBRARY
★
WITHDRAWN
FROM
LIBRARY
STOCK
★
UNIVERSITY OF STRATHCLYDE

DALTON COLLECTING MARSH FIRE GAS

UNIVERSITY OF STRATHCLYDE
27 AUG 1993
UNIVERSITY LIBRARY

Foreword

CIRIA's research programme, *Methane and Associated Hazards to Construction*, is intended to provide guidance for the construction industry, and it consists of a series of research projects dealing with different aspects of the problems posed by methane and the other gases found with methane.

This report is the result of a research project carried out under contract to CIRIA by the Fluid Processes Group of the British Geological Survey (NERC) of Keyworth, Nottingham. The report's purpose is to describe the nature, origins, occurrence and hazards of these gases and, thus, to provide the background necessary for construction professionals to appreciate how dangerous these gases are.

Other companion publications of CIRIA on this subject are: SP79, a bibliography of references relevant to methane and construction; R131, a report explaining the detection, measurement and monitoring of methane; and PR5, the results of a study to determine the construction industry's needs for research and information about methane. Stemming from that study, CIRIA is undertaking further projects about how to overcome the problems posed in different construction situations.

Following CIRIA's usual practice, the research project was guided by a Steering Group which comprised:

R.W. Johnson (*Chairman*)	National House-Building Council
P. Willcocks	Department of the Environment CD4
J.R.F. Burdett	Fire Research Station
D. L. Barry	WS Atkins Environmental
M.A. Smith	Clayton Environmental Consultants
J. Sceal	Wardell Armstrong
A.C. Tingley	Kent County Council
R.A.B. Hall	Mott MacDonald Environmental Services

CIRIA's Research Managers for the project were F.M. Jardine and R. Freer.

The project was funded under Phase I of the programme, *Methane and Associated Hazards to Construction*, by:

Department of the Environment, Construction Directorate
National House-Building Council
Anglian Water Services Ltd
Northumbrian Services Ltd
North West Water Ltd
Southern Water Services Ltd
Thames Water plc
Welsh Water plc
Yorkshire Water Services Ltd
Kyle Stewart Design Services Ltd
Sir Robert McAlpine & Sons Ltd

CIRIA gratefully acknowledges the support of these funding organisations and the technical advice and help given not only by the members of the Steering Groups of the methane programme but also by many other experts. In particular, for their advice on the Section dealing with Abbeystead, CIRIA and the authors thank Sir Alan Muir Wood of Sir William Halcrow and Partners, Mr R.J. Ireland of North West Water and Mr R.M. Arah of Binnie and Partners. The authors express their thanks to other members of the Fluid Processes Group, namely A.H. Bath, G.M. Williams and R. Metcalfe.

Preface

The project leading to this report was carried out under contract to CIRIA by the Fluid Processes Group of the British Geological Survey (NERC), Keyworth, Nottingham. It is painfully clear after the recent incidents at Abbeystead and Loscoe that construction professionals should be aware of the possibilities of methane hazards in civil engineering and building works. Methane can form in a large number of different environments and geological strata including coal seams, hydrocarbon deposits, sediments, soils, groundwaters and landfills. As a result it may be difficult to distinguish the different types of methane and how the hazards may arise in different circumstances.

In construction operations all potential sources of methane need to be considered from an early stage. Suitable measures must be taken to confirm their existence and to assess the risks that they pose both during and following construction. The importance of the integration of geological, geochemical and hydrogeological information when attempting to identify a methane source and make a risk assessment must be stressed.

The migration of gas in the ground is governed by a number of factors which are specific to the site or area of concern. Pathways may exist due to the nature of the geology and hydrogeology of the area or as a result of construction disturbances to the ground or due to a combination of these factors. Engineering measures to protect people and property must be based on an understanding of the nature of the methane problem. This report brings together the available knowledge on the nature, sources and behaviour of methane in a form that is useful to the construction industry. By highlighting the principles behind the formation of hazards and stimulating clear thinking about methane problems the report represents an important initial stage for the construction professional seeking a solution to a methane problem.

Dr Peter J Cook
Director
British Geological Survey (NERC)

Contents

List of Figures

List of Tables

Glossary

abiogenic — without the aid of biology, as in the inorganic production of methane.

acetogenesis — the formation of acetic acid by the bacterial breakdown of fatty acids.

acidogenesis — the formation of fatty acids by the bacterial breakdown of organic matter.

adsorption — the physical adhesion of molecules onto a surface.

advection — fluid flow e.g. groundwater movement.

advected — moved by fluid flow.

aerobic — in the presence of oxygen.

anaerobic — in the absence of oxygen.

anthropogenic — produced by humankind.

bacteriogenic — produced by bacteria.

bio-availability — the level of use of a substance to a living organism as a nutrient.

biogenic — produced with the aid of biology, as in the organic production of methane by bacteria or from the thermal degradation of organic matter.

buffer — a chemical that maintains a constant concentration of another chemical in a liquid.

clathrate — a chemical compound with a cage-like molecular structure enclosing a simpler molecule.

diffusion — mass transport due to concentration gradients.

exsolution (exsolved) — coming out of solution i.e. the opposite of dissolving.

fugacity — the effective partial pressure of a gas.

fumarole — a hole or crack in the ground emitting volcanic gases.

hydrates — ice-like compounds of H_2O molecules trapping simpler molecules like methane in their molecular structures.

hydrolysis — chemical decomposition of a substance by water, the water itself also being decomposed.

isotope — atoms of an element with different mass numbers.

kerogen — solid organic matter, usually in buried marine sediments, which is a precursor of petroleum hydrocarbons.

labile — chemically reactive.

leachate — liquid that has seeped through and out of a landfill.

liquid scintillation	the production of light flashes by the passage of ionising radiation through a liquid.
lipid	a water insoluble organic chemical compound, an ester of a fatty acid.
mafic (ultramafic)	a geological term describing basic igneous rocks containing ferromagnesian minerals; more of these minerals are in ultramafic than mafic rocks.
maturation	the thermal conversion of organic matter in sediments as they are buried.
methanogenesis	the formation of methane by bacterial action.
pH	the measure of acidity (a pH less than neutral which is pH 7) and alkalinity (a pH more than 7) of water and aqueous liquids.
partial pressure	the pressure exerted by a specific gas in a mixture of gases. The sum of the partial pressures is the total pressure.
phreatic zones	a zone where groundwater interacts with magma or lava, often to produce steam.
recharge temperatures	the temperature of water percolating through the unsaturated zone towards the water table of an aquifer to replenish or recharge the aquifer.
redox	shorthand for reduction/oxidation.
sorption	the physical and chemical fixation of molecules to a surface.
stoichiometric	combined in chemical proportion.
substrates	nutrient material for bacteria.
thermogenic	produced by the action of heat, as in the thermal degradation of organic matter to give natural gas.
tholeiitic	the adjective of tholeiite, a basaltic type of igneous rock.
venturi effect	the creation of a low pressure zone when a wind passes over a structure.

Acronyms

BGS	British Geological Survey
CBM	Coal Bed Methane
DoE	Department of the Environment
ETSU	Energy Technology Support Unit, Harwell
LEL	Lower Explosion Limit
SMOW	Standard Mean Ocean Water
STEL	Short Term Exposure Limit
STP	Standard Temperature and Pressure ($0°C$ or 273 K and 1 atmosphere)
TOC	Total Organic Carbon
UEL	Upper Explosion Limit

Chemical Symbols

Ar	argon
C	carbon
^{14}C	carbon-14 isotope; similarly for ^{13}C and ^{12}C
$C_2 - C_4$	alkanes
Ca	calcium
CH_3COO	acetate
CH_3OH	methanol
CH_4	methane
Cl	chlorine
CO	carbon monoxide
CO_2	carbon dioxide
F	fluorine
Fe	iron
H_2	hydrogen
^1H	hydrogen-1 isotope
^2H	deuterium i.e. hydrogen-2 isotope
H_2O	water
HCHO	formaldehyde
HCOOH	formic acid
He	helium
H_2S	hydrogen sulphide
K	potassium
Kr	krypton
Mg	magnesium
Mn	manganese
Na	sodium
Ne	neon
S	sulphur
Xe	xenon

1 Introduction

1.1 PURPOSE AND SCOPE OF THE REPORT

In the long-term, the gradual build-up in the atmosphere of the 'greenhouse' gases methane and carbon dioxide, derived largely from the exploitation and burning of fossil carbon and hydrocarbon fuels since the Industrial Revolution, might cause fundamental changes in climate and so affect every living thing. This report, however, is concerned with the short-term hazards of methane as faced by the construction industry. Recently, there have been some tragic accidents involving gases which were either explosive or asphyxiating. As a result of the publicity surrounding these accidents, the common hazards of methane and other gases encountered in the construction industry have become more widely known. It is the function of this report to present a comprehensive description of methane and its hazards to the professions interested in potential or real gas problems in the construction industry. The impact of methane reaches far outside the world of mining, the practice traditionally most familiar with the problems of gases. This report provides a starting point in the process of risk management. It is intended to be an accessible and practical reference document, stimulating thought not only for construction professionals of different disciplines but for students and those new to the subject.

This report, therefore, provides guidance on the nature, origins, occurrences and hazards of methane. Methane originating from natural soils and rocks and landfills is the primary subject of this project, but the relevance of other associated gases such as carbon dioxide, carbon monoxide, sulphur dioxide, hydrogen sulphide and hydrogen are also considered insofar as they contribute to the hazards of methane.

The project covers the following topics:

1. The formation of methane in the ground.

2. The sources from which methane originates in the ground, including coal measures, hydrocarbon accumulations, peat, sediments and man-made landfills and waste deposits.

3. The movement of methane through the ground as a gas or in solution in groundwater and into construction works.

4. The physical and chemical nature of methane, in particular those properties which contribute to the hazards.

5. The hazards posed by methane and associated gases for different types of construction situations.

6. Illustrative examples of the occurrence, movement or build-up of methane which would put persons or property at risk; the examples include different types and stages of construction projects and, where appropriate, interactions between the construction operations and the possible creation of hazards.

7. Sources of information and reference for safe working practices, for design measures and for construction monitoring and control.

The methods available for detecting, sampling, measuring and monitoring methane and the associated gases are the subject of a companion report prepared for CIRIA by the Fire Research Station, *The measurement of methane and other gases from the ground* (Crowhurst and Manchester, 1993).

The guidance provided by this project covers situations throughout the construction process, including design, construction and maintenance, from the first investigation of a site to the operation of the finished works, in relation to current Health and Safety regulations and any other requirements for safe working practices.

Additional matters included in the report are summary descriptions of published case histories and notes of topics about which there is insufficient knowledge.

Methane from one source or another is often a major feature of gas problems which might affect the development of contaminated land or the construction of tunnels, shafts or buildings. The emphasis, therefore, is placed on methane, although carbon dioxide is often associated with methane and can be of equal danger to human life. Although the ingress of radon (a radioactive, carcinogenic gas) into engineered structures may follow the same pathways and migration mechanisms of methane, it is not covered in this report. Methane is the principal subject of this report, which covers its origins and movements in the ground to the point of entry into a building or construction works.

1.2 NEEDS OF THE CONSTRUCTION INDUSTRY FOR GUIDANCE

The construction industry works in and on the ground — an environment beset with risks. In 1987, the Standing Committee on Structural Safety of the Institutions of Civil and Structural Engineers highlighted the risks of methane in unvented spaces and recommended that the relevant information on methane be compiled and made available to the industry through CIRIA. The information and facts about methane are widely dispersed in the literature and this document attempts to draw that knowledge together in a form which will be useful for the industry. The report summarises the basis of our understanding of methane and its behaviour, whether in the natural environment, confined spaces or engineered traps, in order that planners and engineers can more readily identify likely sources of gas and recognise gas hazards. They will also be able to make a better assessment of the extent of a problem on the basis of the site history, geology, hydrogeology etc. Understanding the scale of the hazard has the advantage of better decision-making in the assessment of how to manage the associated risk.

In its closing two sections, the report illustrates in a general way a number of different construction scenarios where methane can be a hazard and outlines some case histories in order to demonstrate lessons that have been learnt from them. An interaction matrix is used as an aid in thinking about methane. The interaction matrix approach makes for a greater appreciation and awareness of how different factors can influence the creation or removal of gas hazards. The construction process itself is an interactive factor that may have important effects on the ground environment leading to methane hazards. The matrix approach is a useful means of clearly defining a methane problem and indicates how construction professionals might ask the relevant questions concerning gas hazards in their projects.

The report attempts to give some guidance on improving the basis of the decision-making process required to make a risk assessment and to sort out a problem. It is hoped that the setting out of principles will help construction professionals avoid potential problems when planning, designing and constructing new works. Better informed engineering judgements should contribute to greater safety in the different stages leading to the finished works and their maintenance or operation. Consistent, rational procedures for methane site investigations and the protection of existing and new developments are urgently required and are the subjects of future, separate CIRIA reports. Prescriptive solutions to methane gas problems lie outside the remit of this document.

1.3 DIFFERENT CONSTRUCTION SITUATIONS OPEN TO GAS HAZARDS

It is not always appreciated that a methane hazard can arise at different stages of a construction programme, from its starting with the site investigation through to operation and maintenance.

The hazards from methane and other gases in mining are well documented and the management of the risks involved are well established and controlled by legislation. Other construction situations at possible risk are:

- tunnelling and underground civil engineering projects

- constructing dams, in-ground cutoffs and excavations, shafts, wells and boreholes. Vertical structures in the ground which may act as collection points for different gases arriving by diffusion or other means, including transport by water flow

- excavation of trenches, pits, cuttings etc., which may become filled with gases

- building on contaminated land and made-up ground

- natural gas pipes being damaged during construction and releasing mains gas

- work operations in docklands and off-shore involving river, tidal and marine muds, silts and sediments

- finished works, including but not limited to those which contain basements or undercrofts, where there is subsequent incursion of methane from the ground. Ingress of gas into buildings often occurs *via* underground service ducts, drains and pipe or cable runs

- subsequent degradation of building materials leading to the production of methane or other gases.

Construction changes the environment and may have profound effects on the characteristics and properties of the ground, including the gas and groundwater regimes. The construction itself may generate gas traps, extend or create pathways or indeed new sources of gas generation. If land is redeveloped, the legacy of old sewers and other features left behind has to be considered for methane hazards. The key issue is to check the composition of the ground and soil gases in the context of the site history, geography, geology and hydrogeology. Recognition of all possible hazards is the starting point for avoiding gas problems in construction.

2 The nature of methane and some associated gases

In the following sections the properties of methane and other gases (namely carbon dioxide, carbon monoxide, hydrogen sulphide and hydrogen) which are most relevant to construction situations are described. Section 2.1 lists basic chemical and physical properties. Section 2.2 discusses the properties of individual gases and gas mixtures which may cause them to be classed as hazardous. These are primarily their flammability characteristics and physiological effects both on human beings and on plant life. A knowledge of these properties is important when attempting to assess the potential hazards associated with the gases.

2.1 PHYSICAL AND CHEMICAL PROPERTIES

The physical and chemical properties of methane, carbon dioxide, carbon monoxide, hydrogen sulphide and hydrogen are listed below (Edwards, 1989; Sharp, 1987). The composition of air is shown in Table 5 in Appendix A. Methane is the most abundant organic chemical in the Earth's atmosphere and its concentration has been increasing since the Industrial Revolution. The compositions of methane-containing gases are given in Table 6. STP refers to standard temperature and pressure, i.e. a pressure of 1 atmosphere (1.013×10^5 Pascals or 760 mm of mercury or 1.013 bar) and a temperature of 273.15 Kelvin (0°C). Volumes of gases are expressed in volume % or, where smaller volumes are concerned, parts per million (ppm). 1 ppm = 1×10^{-4} volume %; and 1 volume % = 10,000 ppm. Sometimes gas concentrations are reported in mol %, which is equivalent to volume %. A mole of gas occupies 22.4 litres at STP. Concentrations of dissolved gases are often quoted either in mg of gas per litre of water or in mol/l; the advantage is that mass and moles of gas are independent of temperature. Otherwise dissolved gases are given in units of ml STP of gas per litre of water.

2.1.1 Methane

Methane, CH_4, density 0.71 g/l, melting point −184°C, boiling point −164°C. Methane is a colourless, odourless, flammable gas which has a very low solubility in water at STP, although its solubility increases with pressure (see Section 2.1.7). Methane is most commonly produced by the anaerobic degradation of organic material. It is chemically fairly inert but it reacts explosively with chlorine or bromine in the presence of direct sunlight at STP. As a consequence of its infrared adsorption spectrum, methane is an important greenhouse gas in the climate system; a detailed review of the biogeochemical effects of atmospheric methane is given in Cicerone and Oremland (1988).

2.1.2 Carbon dioxide

Carbon dioxide, CO_2, density 1.98 g/l, sublimes at −78.5°C. Carbon dioxide is a colourless, odourless gas with a slightly acid taste at high concentrations. It is non-combustible and is very soluble in water, forming a corrosive liquid (due to the formation of carbonic acid, H_2CO_3) with pH values down to 4. Its high density results in carbon dioxide-rich gas mixtures accumulating in low areas. Figure 1 depicts the density variations for different mixtures of carbon dioxide and methane relative to the density of air.

Locally, carbon dioxide can occur in atmospheric concentrations higher than its average in air as a result of oxidation and combustion of organic materials and from respiration. Equally, local reductions are possible through its removal from the air during photosynthesis in green plants. It is a major constituent of landfill and sewage gas. The atmospheric concentration of carbon dioxide has increased from about 280 ppm to 360 ppm over the last 100 years (Wolman, 1990), causing concern over global warming due to its effect as a greenhouse gas.

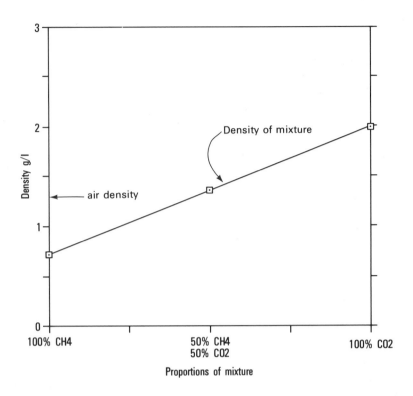

Figure 1 *Density plot for methane/carbon dioxide mixtures*

2.1.3 Carbon monoxide

Carbon monoxide, CO, density 1.25 g/l, melting point $-205°C$, boiling point $-191°C$. Carbon monoxide is a colourless, odourless and tasteless gas. It is produced during the incomplete combustion of organic materials. It is commonly formed after explosions of flammable gas or coal dust and is present during fires. It is soluble in alcohol and benzene, slightly soluble in water and explosive in air.

2.1.4 Hydrogen sulphide

Hydrogen sulphide, H_2S, density 1.53 g/l, melting point $-85°C$, boiling point $-61°C$. Hydrogen sulphide is a colourless gas having the characteristic smell of 'rotten eggs' at low concentrations. It is soluble in water and certain organic solvents e.g. petroleum, and is flammable. Hydrogen sulphide is produced by the decomposition of organic matter containing sulphur and is thus commonly found in the vicinity of sewage treatment plants.

2.1.5 Hydrogen

Hydrogen, H_2, density 0.09 g/l, melting point $-259.14°C$, boiling point $-252.87°C$. Hydrogen is a colourless, odourless and tasteless gas. It is slightly soluble in aqueous and alcoholic solutions. It is a non-toxic, combustible gas.

2.1.6 Landfill gas

Landfill gas consists of a range of gases. The types of gas generated depend primarily on the nature of the fill, the oxygen content of the fill and the hydrogeological conditions. Landfill gas comprises predominantly methane (commonly up to 65% but concentrations greater than this are not unknown) and carbon dioxide. Other gaseous components of landfill gas include hydrogen sulphide and numerous trace organic compounds, including alkenes, alkanes, cycloalkanes, aromatic hydrocarbons, halogenated compounds, organosulphur compounds, alcohols, esters and ethers (Brookes and Young, 1983). The gas composition changes in a landfill have been described by Lawson and Alston (1989) and the main features are shown in Figure 11 in Section 3.3.1.

2.1.7 Gas solubilities

Methane, carbon dioxide etc. may not always exist in the subsurface in the gaseous form; they may well be dissolved in groundwater to an extent depending on the pressure, temperature and the concentration of other gases or minerals in the water. Pressure has the most dominant effect on methane concentration in water. Gas solubilities increase with pressure according to Henry's Law, a detailed explanation of which is given in Appendix A.2. From the data in Tables 5 and 7, it can be shown that air-saturated water at 10°C in equilibrium with air at normal atmospheric pressure will contain 4.78×10^{-5} mg of methane per litre of water, equivalent to 6.70×10^{-5} ml STP methane per litre of water. Note that the conversion of mg/l to ml STP/l is effected by means of the ideal gas equation (see Appendix A.2) and is easily done for the case of methane (molecular weight 16 and remembering that the volume of a mole of gas at STP is 22.4 litres) by multiplying the mg/l value by the factor 22.4/16 i.e. 1.4.

When the partial pressure of methane reaches 1 atmosphere at 10°C, the water in equilibrium saturation will hold 29.9 mg of methane per litre of water or 41.9 ml STP per litre of water (using the relevant Henry's Law constant in Table 7). Interestingly, a slightly different solubility (30.9 mg per litre of water) is evident from the datum in Table 8 using the Ostwald coefficient for methane in water.

Temperature effects

The solubilities of most gases fall with increasing temperature up to the critical temperature of the solvent. Methane solubility in water declines from 0 to 100°C but increases by a factor of twenty between 100 and 350°C (Drummond, 1981). Gas solubilities in water from temperatures of 10°C to 75°C are listed in Table 8 of Appendix A.2. Air-saturated water at 25°C and atmospheric pressure will contain 3.56×10^{-5} mg of methane per litre of water, equivalent to 4.98×10^{-5} ml STP methane per litre of water (according to the data in Tables 5 and 8). Note that these concentration values are smaller than for 10°C.

Pressure effects

The solubilities of gases show a marked rise with increasing pressure, the solubilities of most gases being approximately linear functions of pressure. This is an alternative way of expressing Henry's Law, i.e. the mass of gas dissolved by a given volume of solvent is proportional to the partial pressure of the gas with which it is in equilibrium (see Appendix A.2).

The salting-out effect

Solubilities of gases are often quoted with respect to distilled or pure water. Natural waters usually contain varying amounts of dissolved salts which lower gas solubility. This is known as the 'salting-out' effect. This is described by the Setschenow equation (Setschenow, 1889) which postulates that at a constant temperature the logarithm of solubility is a linear function of salt concentration.

2.1.8 Gas viscosities

Viscosity can be defined as the internal resistance of the fluid to flow (Amyx *et al.*, 1960). Viscosity is a function of temperature, pressure and molecular weight of the fluid. A knowledge of the viscosity of fluids is needed when estimating the rate of flow of fluids through rocks or sediments. Gases may move through a porous medium such as sediment or rock by viscous flow under a pressure gradient, and flow rates can be estimated using Darcy's Law (see Appendix F.4). The variation in gas viscosity at atmospheric pressure with temperature is shown in Figure 41. In certain cases it may be necessary to estimate the viscosity of a gas mixture, for example when calculating flow rates of landfill gas which is primarily composed of a mixture of methane and carbon dioxide. A method for the calculation of gas viscosity is given in Appendix A.3.

2.1.9 Gaseous diffusion

In addition to viscous flow, gases may also move by molecular diffusion caused by the presence of a concentration gradient. Gas diffusion rates can be calculated using Fick's Law (see Sections 6.1.1 & Appendix F.3). Diffusion coefficients vary according to the type of porous medium and its degree of saturation. Diffusion coefficients for methane in various media are listed in Table 9.

2.2 HAZARDOUS PROPERTIES

There are many situations where the composition of the ambient atmosphere may differ considerably from that of normal air (see Table 5). This may be caused either by the incursion of gas from an external source or by the removal of a gas component. The result may be an atmosphere that is asphyxiating, explosive or toxic.

Gaseous emissions of a toxic, flammable or asphyxiant nature, emanating from contaminated sites or due to natural phenomena may represent both short- and long-term hazards depending on the nature of the gas, the geological conditions and the proximity and extent of building development.

The important properties of individual gases and gas mixtures in relation to their associated hazards are their flammability characteristics, solubility and physiological effects. These are dealt with in the following sections. The limiting values of common gas contaminants for toxicity or asphyxiation and explosive limits in air are listed in Table 10.

2.2.1 Flammability characteristics of various methane/gas mixtures

The greatest hazards posed by methane are those of fire and/or explosion. In this section the explosive properties of various methane/gas mixtures are discussed. The limits of flammability of gas mixtures are affected by the composition of the mixture, strength of the ignition source, temperature, pressure and the nature of the surroundings (Edwards, 1989).

Methane forms an explosive mixture with air when the concentration is between 5% and 15% by volume. The 5% volume is called the Lower Explosive Limit (LEL), and 5% concentration by volume is equivalent to 100% LEL. The 15% volume is called the Upper Explosive Limit (UEL). It should be emphasised that concentrations above the UEL should not be taken to represent safety in terms of the likelihood of an explosion. Where carbon dioxide is also present, the range of volume concentration of methane which is explosive is narrowed, and when the proportion of carbon dioxide reaches 25 volume % the methane becomes non-flammable.

An increase in the initial temperature of the methane/air mixture will widen the limits of flammability, e.g. between 370°C and 427°C the limits become 3.25 and 29.1 volume % methane respectively for the LEL and UEL. If the oxygen content of the methane-air mixture is reduced, the limits of flammability are narrowed, e.g. at 13.45 volume % of oxygen the lower and upper limits are respectively 6.5 and 7 volume % methane, whilst at 13.25 volume % oxygen the mixture is incapable of propagating a flame. The temperature needed to cause explosion is 650 to 750°C i.e. a spark is sufficient. The explosive wave of methane and oxygen has a velocity of 2322 m/s but the flame speed is slower. When methane is mixed with hydrogen the explosive range is greatly extended.

The limits of flammability of a mixture of gases can be calculated by means of Le Chatelier's Law. The limit, L (upper or lower), is given by:

$$L = \frac{100}{\left(\dfrac{p_1}{N_1} + \dfrac{p_2}{N_2} + \dfrac{p_3}{N_3} + \cdots \right)}$$

where
p_1, p_2, p_3 = proportions of each flammable gas present in the mixture
N_1, N_2, N_2 = the limit of flammability of each flammable gas separately.

The ratio of inert gas to the flammable components is an important factor in determining the limits of flammability of gas mixtures. Further data on the flammability of various gas mixtures are given in Edwards (1989). Hydrogen forms explosive mixtures with air in the range 4 to 74 volume % hydrogen. Hydrogen is considered to be one of the most dangerous flammable gases because of its low ignition energy and wide limits of flammability. Carbon monoxide and hydrogen sulphide also have wide limits of flammability (see Table 10).

2.2.2 Conditions leading to gaseous explosions

A flammable gas or gas mixture is potentially hazardous when conditions exist which allow the gas to migrate from its source and accumulate in a confined area in sufficient concentrations to allow ignition.

Gases may move through rocks either by movement through voids if the rock or sediment is permeable and has an interconnected porosity, or through joints or fractures (see Section 6). Gases may also be dissolved in groundwater and may be released as the water enters natural or man-made voids, or as pressure conditions change. Leachate from landfill sites may also contain dissolved gases or may degrade during migration from the site to produce methane with carbon dioxide and associated gases.

A flammable mixture of gas or vapour and air burns rapidly when ignited. If confined the deflagration generates high explosive overpressures. Each of the following three conditions must be fulfilled for an explosion to take place (Beresford, 1989):

1. There must be a source of flammable gas or vapour.

2. There must be an enclosed space in which the gas or vapour can accumulate with sufficient air to form a flammable mixture. Examples are building foundations, enclosed basements; voids such as trenches, shafts or boreholes may also allow methane accumulation.

3. There must be a source of ignition. Examples are electric lighting, electric motors, sparks from metal to metal contact, cutting and welding equipment, cigarette smoking etc.

Areas of work activity in which problems with methane may potentially occur have been identified (Barry, 1986; Lamont, 1989; Creedy, 1991a). These include civil engineering and tunnelling operations, landfilling operations, the construction and operation of water abstraction boreholes, mains gas distribution, coal and mineral mining and any form of construction which involves the use of former, completed landfill sites or contaminated land.

2.2.3 Solubility effects

Dissolved gases are present in groundwater. When the pressure on a groundwater is reduced and the solubility limits of the gases in the water are exceeded, the gases bubble out of solution and form a separate gaseous phase. A pressure decrease will occur, for example, whenever a tunnel is excavated or when a borehole is drilled. The explosion at Abbeystead (see Section 7.3) occurred because groundwater containing methane at a lithostatic/ hydrostatic pressure of several hundred metres entered the tunnel which was at atmospheric pressure. The methane came out of solution in the same way that carbon dioxide bubbles out of a lemonade bottle when the top is unscrewed. An example which shows the effect of pressure release on methane-saturated water is given in Section 6.5.4.

2.2.4 Physiological effects

The physiological hazards of chemicals are dependent not only upon the toxicity of materials but also upon degree and nature of exposure (Croner, 1991). The effects produced may appear in both the short and the long term. Local effects are produced at the point of contact, whereas systemic effects are those produced by the chemical or its metabolites (breakdown products) on a whole range of bodily functions often far removed from the route of entry into the body. Effects may occur in the short-term or may be delayed. The physiological effects of exposure to methane, carbon dioxide, carbon monoxide, hydrogen sulphide and hydrogen are described below.

The exposure limits are taken from the Health and Safety Executive Guidance Note EH40, which is revised annually. The exposure limits listed in the following sections refer to airborne concentrations of substances and represent conditions under which it is believed that nearly all workers may be exposed daily without adverse effect (Croner, 1991). The long-term exposure limit is based on an 8-hour reference period, and the short-term exposure limit (STEL) is based on a 10-minute reference period.

Methane

Methane is classed as a low toxicity gas but can be a simple asphyxiant due to the displacement of oxygen. Symptoms of oxygen starvation develop at around 33 volume % methane and a concentration of 75 volume % results in fatality within minutes.

Carbon dioxide

Carbon dioxide is classed as a highly toxic chemical. Exposure limits: 8 hours at 5000 ppm, STEL 10 minutes at 15000 ppm. At concentrations of 3 volume %, shortness of breath and headache will occur, these symptoms becoming severe at 5 to 6 volume %. At levels of 10 to 11 volume %, headache, visual distortion, tremors and rapid loss of consciousness occur. Concentrations of 22 volume % or more are likely to be fatal. The high solubility of carbon dioxide results in rapid diffusion into the blood and physiological effects are almost instantaneous. If elevated carbon dioxide concentrations are accompanied by a reduction in oxygen concentration the effects will be more severe.

Carbon monoxide

Carbon monoxide is classified as a highly toxic chemical. Exposure limits: 8 hours at 50 ppm, STEL 10 minutes at 300 ppm. Carbon monoxide has a much greater affinity for haemoglobin than oxygen and forms carboxyhaemaglobin, thus preventing oxygen being transported in the body. The effects of various concentrations of carbon monoxide in air are related to several factors (Edwards, 1989), the initial concentration in the blood, the concentration in the air, the length of exposure and the level of activity of the individual. Concentrations of 60 to 80 % saturation of carboxyhaemoglobin can be fatal.

Hydrogen sulphide

Hydrogen sulphide is classed as a highly toxic chemical, approximately five times as toxic as carbon monoxide and almost as toxic as hydrogen cyanide. Exposure limits: 8 hours at 10 ppm, STEL 10 minutes at 15 ppm. Despite its odour which is detectable at levels as low as 0.025 ppm, high concentrations producing toxic effects can be reached almost without warning because of a loss of sense of smell (olfactory fatigue) at about 50 ppm. At concentrations of 20 to 150 ppm redness and watering of the eyes, blurred vision, sore throat, coughing and shortness of breath can occur. At concentrations of 400 to 500 ppm, pulmonary oedema, headache, dizziness, coma and asphyxiation may occur.

Hydrogen

Hydrogen is classed as a non-toxic, simple asphyxiant.

Trace organic components

There are many trace components in landfill gas and some of these may have toxic and/or carcinogenic properties. However, the trace components are usually present in very low concentrations and considerable air dilution may take place as the gases migrate. Volatile organic compounds may pose a high degree of risk in a post-construction phase when the occupants of a building may become exposed. It should be emphasised that the type and concentration of trace components is very site specific.

2.2.5 Effects on vegetation

Strong correlations appear to exist between high concentrations of methane and/or carbon dioxide in soil and vegetation die-back (Barry, 1986), especially in areas surrounding landfill sites. Current evidence indicates that carbon dioxide is toxic to vegetation and that the principal effect of methane is to produce oxygen deficiency in the root zone (Barry, 1986). A combination of both gases is therefore likely to be additive and especially serious at times of critical plant growth such as germination. The apparent ease with which some plant species grow on landfill sites cannot always be interpreted as plant tolerance but might merely reflect the fact that gas is not reaching the plant roots in that area, or that the gas composition is not critical. Similarly, when die-back does occur it should not be assumed to be the result solely of gas effects, because other causes are possible from ground contamination by chemicals, poor soil structure, nutrient deficiency, drainage problems or any combination of these.

Most soils contain microbes which are capable of oxidising methane to produce carbon dioxide if air is present (see Section 5). Thus in soils in which methane oxidation is occurring, effects relevant to vegetation growth are the depletion of the oxygen content, the production of carbon dioxide and heating (see Figure 15). Where the oxygen content is low the conversion of methane to carbon dioxide may be incomplete and intermediate products such as methanol, formaldehyde and formic acid may be produced. These can remain in the soil and exhibit direct toxicity to plants. Hydrogen sulphide, ammonia, benzene, ethylene, acetaldehyde and mercaptans which are often present in association with landfill gas are known to be highly toxic to plants (Kanol and Zetther, 1990).

3 Origins and sources of methane

Methane (or marsh gas) was discovered in 1800 by the famous chemist John Dalton who lived in Manchester, and collected his samples from the many peat marshes that surrounded the city. Methane is the most abundant organic compound in the Earth's atmosphere; its occurrences in the Earth's crust are predominantly of biogenic origin, i.e. their ultimate source is biologically formed organic material. Methane can also be formed through inorganic reactions and this type of methane is consequently termed abiogenic.

Methane is a highly reduced form of carbon, and together with carbon dioxide plays an important role in many geochemical processes in the Earth's crust. Methane formation is observed in extremely different environments. In recent sediments, methane is produced (and consumed) by microbial processes, and in the oceans may be preserved in methane hydrates. In deeper sections of the Earth's crust, methane is a product of the conversion of organic matter under the influence of elevated temperatures (natural gas associated with coal and petroleum) and deeper still methane is found in metamorphic rocks. Methane is also found emanating with geothermal waters and steams on continents and hot water vents at oceanic spreading centres. However, in volcanic and geothermal environments carbon dioxide and other gases are more of a hazard than methane. Landfill, waste management practices and many other human activities give rise to methane sources of concern to the construction industry. Figure 2 shows a number of sources of subsurface methane.

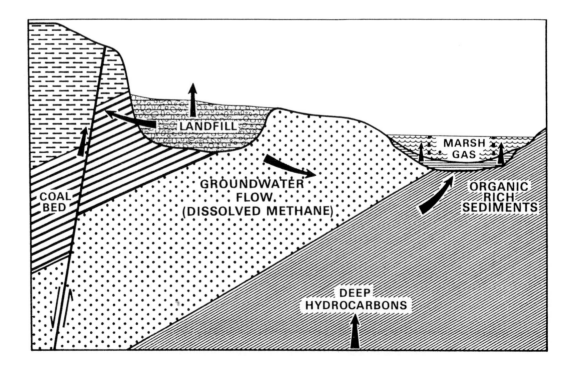

Figure 2 *Sources of sub-surface methane*

3.1 NATURAL CONCENTRATIONS OF GASES IN THE GROUND

Methane is found in a number of different physical states and a knowledge of these is fundamental to an understanding of the processes controlling the occurrence and distribution of sub-surface methane.

'Free' methane gas may be found in pores, fractures and cavities in soils, rocks and sediments of all types and also as bubbles in water or modern marine sediments.

Adsorbed methane is found in high concentrations on coals and other carbonaceous materials. Fine pores within coals provide vast surface areas on to which gas molecules can be tightly packed, so tightly that the density of the gas approaches that of a liquid.

Methane can also be present in solution in groundwaters. Methane has a very low solubility at atmospheric pressure but at elevated pressures significant volumes can be held in solution (see Section 2.1.7). Table 1 shows the annual methane release rates from various sources.

Table 1 Annual methane release rates from various sources (after Large, 1983)

Source	Amount produced (tonnes $CH_4 \times 10^6$ per year)
Bacteriogenic sources	
Enteric fermentation of ruminants	101 − 220
Paddy fields	280
Swamps and marshes	130 − 260
Fresh-water lakes	1.25 − 25
Other	5.27 − 16.5
Total	528 − 812
Anthropogenic and volcanic sources	
Coal mining	6.3 − 22
Lignite mining	1.6 − 5.7
Industrial losses	7 − 21
Automobile exhaust	0.5
Volcanic	0.2
Total	15.6 − 49.4

3.1.1 In soils

Generally, background concentrations of methane in soil gas vary between 0.2 and 1.6 ppm, the latter being the mean concentration of methane in air (see Table 5). Much higher soil gas methane concentrations may be found in soils adjacent to landfill sites if a migration pathway is available. Methane concentrations above 0.1 volume % (1000 ppm) are rarely encountered in soil gas in the absence of an identifiable source (Butterworth, 1991). In areas close to landfill sites, the distribution and concentration of methane in soil gas at shallow depths (less than 2 m) may be used to give a general indication of the direction of movement of contaminated groundwater (Barber et al., 1990).

Soils develop as a result of a series of physical, chemical and biological transformations of rock during weathering. Apart from minerals, soils contain living organisms and undecomposed organic substances as well as water and gases. A useful précis of the physical, chemical and microbiological structures of soils is given by Grant and Long (1981). The composition of gas in soils, i.e. soil gas, is determined by a number of factors: biological oxygen consumption with the production of carbon dioxide; solution and sorption processes in the soil; and gas exchange with the free atmosphere.

The composition of soil gas is different from that in the atmosphere. The most important differences are a reduction in oxygen content and an increase in carbon dioxide as a result of biological activity; the nitrogen content is generally similar to that in air (Matthess, 1982).

The average oxygen and carbon dioxide contents of the free atmosphere are 20.95 volume % and 0.03 volume % respectively. The oxygen and carbon dioxide contents of soil gas vary as a result of biological processes occurring within the soil. Carbon dioxide is produced and oxygen is consumed through the respiratory processes of plant roots and microbial activity. These processes cause a gradual increase of the carbon dioxide concentration with depth from about 0.03 % at the soil surface to, for example, about 1 to 5 % below the plant rooting zone. Root depths vary according to the plant type, e.g. 25-50 cm for wheat but several metres for trees. The oxygen content of soil gas may also vary with depth and on a daily and annual basis (Bolt and Bruggenwert, 1976).

The carbon dioxide content of the atmosphere (0.03 volume %) has seen a small but significant increase over the last century due to the burning of fossil fuels. It varies over rural environments between 0.021 and 0.044 volume % and can be higher locally in the vicinity of industry, towns, hot springs and volcanic emanations. The carbon dioxide content in soil gas may be 10 to 100 times higher than the associated atmosphere. This is due to the effect of acids such as nitric acid or sulphuric acid on carbonates as well as the production of carbon dioxide by bacteria in the soil. Values between 0.1 and 5 volume % are common (Fernandez and Kosian, 1987) and occasionally even higher values (up to 20 volume %) have been observed directly above the water table. Higher values occur in the vicinity of natural escapes of carbon dioxide such as volcanic emanations and hydrothermal gases (see Appendix B).

In a review of the occurrences of carbon dioxide in soil gas not associated with landfills, coal mines or leaking gas mains, Butterworth (1991) found that published information is sparse and often related to special circumstances such as the presence of underground ore bodies. These include pyritic subcrops, lignite deposits and the lead-zinc ore body at Navan in Ireland, where values of up to 10 % carbon dioxide were detected in the soils. He concluded that values of greater than 5 % carbon dioxide in soil gas composition seem generally to reflect special circumstances. In areas of man-made pollution where groundwater is contaminated with organic compounds, soil gas compositions containing 26 volume % carbon dioxide have been measured (Bishop *et al.*, 1966).

As well as nitrogen, oxygen, carbon dioxide and methane, other gases such as ammonia, nitrous oxide and hydrogen sulphide may occur in soil gas. Hydrogen sulphide and methane may be present as products of putrefaction. Results of soil gas investigations may be used for the detection of contaminant sources within the boundaries of a pollution plume and to define areas to be designated for remedial action (Godoy and Naleid, 1990).

3.1.2 In groundwaters

Normal shallow groundwaters in the U.K. have very low background concentrations of methane (as far as is known from limited data) which may be a reflection of either chemical equilibrium *in situ* or of steady state concentrations determined by migration from deeper strata into the active groundwater systems. Table 2 displays available methane data for some UK groundwaters. These data suggest that in general the abundance of methane tends to increase with depth in groundwater systems, probably due to a combination of factors including degradation of indigenous traces of organics in the rock phase, influx of methane from other sources, and slower groundwater movements at depth.

The different sources of methane in the U.K. groundwaters are not reliably known. However, the origins of some simpler gases in groundwater are easier to explain. During the recharge or replenishment of an aquifer, groundwater percolates through the unsaturated zone to the underlying water table and equilibrates with the gases in the atmosphere of the unsaturated zone. The infiltrating groundwater therefore contains gases dissolved at concentrations reflecting their partial pressures and temperature in the unsaturated zone. Measurement of the inert gas (He, Ne, Ar, Kr, Xe) concentrations and the application of temperature-dependences of their solubilities can yield estimates of the temperatures involved. Such information from old groundwaters has been related to palaeoclimates (Mazor, 1972; Bath *et al.*, 1979; Andrews, 1987; Andrews and Wilson, 1987; Andrews *et al.*, 1984; Andrews *et al.*, 1989). However, there is a complicating factor; these atmospheric gases tend to be present in groundwaters at slightly supersaturated concentrations as a result of the so-called 'excess air' phenomenon (Heaton and Vogel, 1981). 'Excess air' is dissolved into groundwaters, it is thought, from the entrainment of small air bubbles in the unsaturated zone, these bubbles soon being assumed into solution as the hydrostatic pressure increases below the water table.

Table 2 Methane concentrations in some UK groundwaters

Groundwater location	Methane concentration (ml STP per litre water)	Partial pressure of methane (atm)	T (°C)
[1] In Chalk, London Basin, >70 m depth.	< 1.7 x 10^2	< 4.0 x 10^4	10
[2] Crystalline and metamorphic rocks, Scotland.	< 1.3 x 10^{-5}	< 3.1 x 10^{-7}	10
[3] In brines of Permo-Trias, Wessex Basin, 1700 m depth.	1.8	0.096	70
[4] Carboniferous strata in Abbeystead tunnel.	40	0.955	10

[1]Darling (1985); [2]Darling and Bath (1986); [3]Darling (1981); [4]Bath *et al.* (1988).

The concentration of carbon dioxide dissolved in groundwater is determined by the partial pressure of carbon dioxide in the soil zone, which is often up to 2 or 3 orders of magnitude higher than that in air because of its enhancement by microbial respiration in soil. The actual partial pressure of carbon dioxide is dependent on pH, which might be independently buffered or controlled, and also on equilibria with, for example, calcium carbonate minerals.

A separate gas phase should form only when the partial pressure of a volatile component equals or exceeds the hydrostatic pressure. This is the case in gas-phase accumulations of hydrocarbons which are in contact with formation water or liquid hydrocarbons in sedimentary rock reservoirs. There are also anomalous and rare occurrences of He-, CO_2- and N_2- dominated gas-phase accumulations, although none of these cases is in the U.K. Non-hydrocarbon gas loading in a UK sedimentary basin is typified by the dissolved gases, principally nitrogen, contained in the formation brine of the Permo-Triassic sediments of the Wessex Basin which have a total gas pressure of around 1.6 bar; this is low compared with the hydrostatic pressure of over 170 bar (Darling, 1981).

Edwards (1991) reported several worldwide occurrences of methane in groundwater in Japan, Canada, U.S.A., Hungary and the U.K., covering a wide range of hydrogeological conditions. Dyck *et al.* (1976) found only 14 groundwaters with more than 0.224 ml STP methane per litre of water out of a survey of about 1700 water supply wells in eastern maritime Canada. At least 135 of 150 groundwaters sampled from aquifers in West Germany contained less than 0.045 ml STP of methane per litre of water. High concentrations of methane are relatively common in groundwaters contained within organic-rich shallow glacial and Palaeozoic sediments in Illinois and other parts of the midwestern USA (Coleman *et al.*, 1988). The methane derives from the reduction *in situ* of the organic material under strongly anaerobic conditions and can constitute over 90 % of the dissolved gases; radiocarbon data show that the age of source material is frequently less than 30,000 years which is consistent with its origin in glacial detritus. The oxidation of these relatively large concentrations of methane can lead to characteristic chemistries for associated groundwaters (Kelly *et al.*, 1985; Bath *et al.*, 1988) (see also Section 5.3 and Appendix B.8).

Methane, ultimately of bacteriogenic or thermogenic origin, may find its way into groundwater systems. Barker and Fritz (1981a) sampled 264 groundwater samples in a study of the origin of methane in different groundwaters from 10 field locations in Canada and the U.S.A. These areas covered different hydrogeological systems from Quaternary deposits to crystalline rocks. This survey found methane to be a common trace constituent of groundwaters with methane concentrations ranging from less than 0.0224 to greater than 140 ml STP of methane per litre of water. The use of stable isotope ratios (see Section 4.4) indicated that in the majority of cases the methane had been produced by the anaerobic degradation of organic material.

3.2 GEOLOGICAL SOURCES OF METHANE

Methane can be formed by the anaerobic biochemical reduction of organic matter by micro-organisms, or can be formed over geological periods of time following the burial, compression and heating of organic material. Following Schoell (1988), thermogenic methane is taken to be a type of biogenic methane, derived by thermal degradation of organic matter, while bacteriogenic methane is taken to be a type of biogenic methane generated by microbes. About 80 % of natural gas is of thermogenic origin. Generally, thermogenic methanes can be distinguished from bacteriogenic methanes by their heavier carbon isotope compositions (see Sections 4.4 and 5.5) and by containing light hydrocarbon gases such as ethane, propane, butane, etc.

The hypothesis that the Earth condensed from a cloud of inter-stellar gas containing, amongst other primordial constituents, methane, has been postulated in recent years. Gold and Soter (1980, 1982) have suggested that primordial methane is presently outgassing from the Earth's crust and that earlier emanations had been trapped to form many known hydrocarbon reserves. Gold and Soter observed a correlation between the major oil and gas producing regions and seismically active zones and postulated that fracturing of the Earth's crust during tectonism facilitated migration of methane and associated hydrocarbons. The hypothesis of Gold and Soter has not been widely accepted. While this primordial methane may well exist in the Earth's crust there is at present no evidence to support the view that it could have given rise to the hydrocarbon deposits of the UK (Bath et al., 1986). Other examples of abiogenic methane are described in Appendix B.

3.2.1 Methane in coal measures

Under the influence of normal geothermal temperatures the composition of buried plant remains systematically changes with depth and time liberating hydrocarbon gas as a by-product of the reactions. Coal measures strata originate from vegetation which grew in swamps and deltas, where predominantly terrestrial vegetation decayed, was buried, compressed and heated by sedimentation over a long period of geological time. This process, known as coalification, represents a continuum starting from peat, passing through the lignite and brown coal stage into the high, medium then low volatile bituminous region and culminating with anthracite.

Some evolution of methane and carbon dioxide occurs in the early stages of the accumulation of dead plant debris. However, the major phase of methane generation is thought to occur at a later stage in the coalification process.

Studies into the relationship between the degree of coalification or rank of coal and methane generation in coal seams have estimated a production in the high-volatile bituminous to anthracite range of more than 200 m^3/tonne (Creedy, 1989, 1991b). Although coal adsorbs methane, its adsorption capacity is greatly exceeded by methane production during burial. Such quantities far exceed the quantities now found in coal seams, the highest recorded seam gas contents are of the order of 40 m^3/tonne.

It is probable that much of the gas generated during coalification is dispersed through the surrounding strata and that some is removed in solution as the moisture content of the consolidating rock is progressively reduced. In the coal measures, therefore, methane is invariably adsorbed on coal, or may be trapped in gas pockets or dissolved in groundwater within the whole of the coal measures depositional sequence which is typified by mudstones, siltstones, sandstones, seatearths and coals. Gas that is not dispersed may be trapped in commercially viable natural gas reservoirs.

The *in-situ* methane content of UK coal seams varies between trace and 25 m^3/tonne according to the rank of the coal and its proximity to ancient and present erosion surfaces. Coal seams are excellent gas reservoirs in terms of storage capability but poor producers unless disrupted by strong tectonic activity or disturbed by mining. In 1988 about 43 % of the methane piped to the surface from British Coal mines was either exploited on the colliery site or sold to industrial consumers (Creedy, 1991a). In the USA there has recently been a dramatic increase in coal bed methane (CBM) recovery as a result of a federal tax credit on non-conventional fuels. Production doubled between 1987 and 1989 to 100 billion cubic feet of recovered CBM and volumes of one trillion cubic feet are predicted for 1992 (Carter, 1991).

Methane is often a problem in areas where coal measures occur either at the surface or at depth, due to natural degassing. In the Wigan area, well before the Wigan Coal Field was developed, there were numerous reports of burning wells and of explosions which destroyed housing. It seems that the mines, which subsequently removed the coal reserves, helped to vent the gas from the subsurface so that these remarkable sights disappeared. Old mine shafts into the working will still allow methane to escape to the surface. In general, old closed workings pose a hazard from methane (see Section 7). Coal measures strata occur principally in the Carboniferous and Jurassic deposits of the UK. Figure 3 shows the distribution of coal-bearing strata in the UK.

3.2.2 Methane in other mines and strata

Gases containing methane concentrations from trace to more than 90 volume % have been encountered in a wide range of igneous, metamorphic and sedimentary rock environments associated with various economic deposits including oil-shales, potash, salt, uranium, zinc, copper, lead, diamond, arsenic and apatite (Creedy, 1989) and gold (Naden and Shepherd, 1989) as well as coal. The deposits in which methane has been found range in age from Recent to the Precambrian.

The processes which account for the origin of the bulk of the gas are few. The methane is generally geochemically independent of the inorganic economic minerals and frequently attributable to a carbonaceous source located in strata above, below or laterally adjacent. However, there may be a thermal connection with magmatically associated ores; the igneous activity may be responsible for restarting or enhancing coalification-type reactions leading to increased methane production.

Concentrated organic sediments in the form of coal seams probably account for about 1 % of the total organic matter distributed in the Earth's crust. A large volume of potential methane-generating material is therefore disseminated within the sedimentary pile. Organic matter incorporated in sediments whether in the form of coals, dark mudstones or isolated fragments constitute the most important source of methane.

Williamson (1991) has considered some of the more obvious potential methane source rocks in Britain other than Carboniferous coal-bearing strata. Highly organic-rich horizons which are potential methane producers are particularly associated with carbonaceous or bituminous strata and oil shales.

In the Devonian, oil shales occur in the Orkneys and bituminous shales occur near Strathpeffer in the Northern Highlands of Scotland. Jurassic strata contain major sequences of organic rich shales of which the Jet Rock Formation (Lower Jurassic) and the Oxford and Kimmeridge Clays (Upper Jurassic) are the most significant. In addition the Middle Jurassic sequences of North Yorkshire and Scotland are characterised by a typical development of 'coal measure' type sediments.

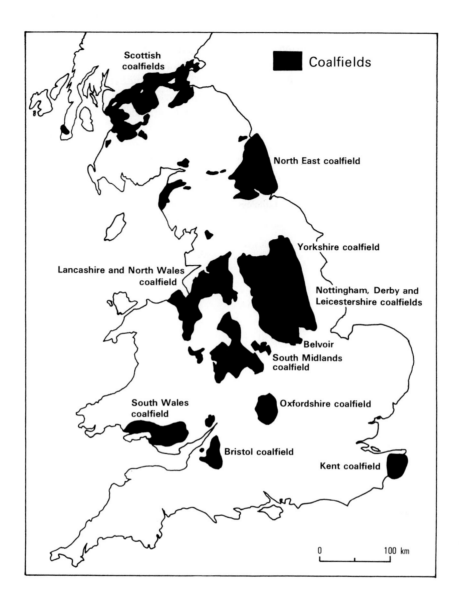

Figure 3 *The coalfields of Britain*

In the Lower Jurassic, oil shales occur in Somerset, and highly bituminous shales are found near Lyme Regis. The Jet Rock formation is particularly developed along the northeast Yorkshire coast near Whitby where the jet, a hard black variety of lignite occurs as isolated masses within richly bituminous shales. Coals, which have been worked in the past, occur in what was originally termed the Estuarine Series in the Cleveland Hills of North Yorkshire. At Brora in the Highland Region of Scotland, the Middle Jurassic rocks contain coal seams associated with highly carbonaceous shales. Oil shales are also present in the Middle Jurassic of the Isles of Skye and Raasay. In the Upper Jurassic, the Lower and Middle Oxford clays usually have a bituminous content. The Kimmeridge clay outcrops extend from Dorset to Yorkshire and also occur in northeast Scotland and the Inner Hebrides, and are associated with thin seams of oil and bituminous shales.

Unexpectedly high amounts of methane gas have been detected in sedimentary Carboniferous strata of the Northern Pennines (Ferguson, 1984). This study involved the measurement of the respective volumes of light hydrocarbon gases (methane, ethane, propane and butane) in samples of sedimentary rocks. Previous work had indicated that the expected amount of methane as a percentage of the total light hydrocarbons in limestones was about 69 %, whereas the Northern Pennines limestones contained up to 97.4 % methane as a percentage of the total light hydrocarbons. Similar trends were found in other Carboniferous strata from the area. Ferguson postulated two origins for the gas: either generation as a direct result of chemical reactions occurring during the mineralization of the area or as a consequence of the prolonged existence of a high geothermal gradient in the area which may have caused thermal degradation of relict organic material within the strata. In this context, relict organic material is that material which was not degraded during the earlier stages of sedimentation. The methane and ethane contents of some UK sedimentary rocks are shown in Table 3.

Table 3 Methane and ethane contents of some UK sedimentary rocks (after Creedy, 1989)

Age	Lithology	Gas Contents (litres/tonne)	
		Methane	Ethane
JURASSIC	Calcareous mudstones	0.1 − 29	0.02 − 0.7
	Limestones	6.7	0.8
CARBONIFEROUS			
Westphalian D	Marl	0.8	0.03
Westphalian A − C	Sandstones	10 − 150	1 − 32
	Siltstones	20 − 60	3 − 16
	Mudstones	10 − 100	2 − 21
	Carbonaceous mudstones	180 − 630	29 − 84 *
Visean-Namurian	Limestones	1.4 - 75	0.2 − 2.8

* Includes adsorbed gas.

3.2.3 Oil and gas

Methane is not only associated with coal. Marine sediments derived from the accumulation of plankton, algae, bacteria and the bodies of dead fish and marine animals gave rise to oil and gas by similar geological processes of burial, compaction and heating (see Figure 4).

As a result of the difference in the original organic material (i.e. plankton rather than the higher terrestrial plants) oil and gas are produced rather than coal. Whereas coal is solid and formed *in situ* where the organic material was deposited, oil and gas migrate to accumulate in a variety of geological traps. There are many different sorts of geological traps (see Figure 5) but all essentially present an impermeable seal to upward migration whilst providing a porous and permeable reservoir rock below. Oil and gas exploration depends largely on the identification of suitable geological structures in which gas may accumulate such as anticlines, domes, faults, and stratigraphic traps.

At typical geothermal gradients in the crust of the UK, the production of methane may extend down to 5 km depth where temperatures up to about 150°C may be reached and in which organic sediments have matured to produce hydrocarbons in the so-called 'oil-' and 'gas-windows' (Tissot and Welte, 1978). Methane is also produced bacteriogenically by the microbial reduction of organic material; this process is particularly common in shallow marine sediments (Claypool and Kvenvolden, 1983). It is not clear to what extent there is deeper microbial activity which might contribute to methane production in conventional hydrocarbon reservoir formation (Schoell, 1988). Thermogenic or biogenic methane can achieve pressures which equal hydrostatic pressure in the subsurface, thereby forming a discrete gas-phase reservoir of the kind that is found in the North Sea (commonly a Carboniferous coal measures source rock expelling methane into a Permian Rotliegendes reservoir; Barnard and Cooper, 1983), and also in the Irish Sea Morecambe Bay gas field (a Carboniferous source rock and a Permo-Trias Sherwood or St Bees Sandstone reservoir; Ebbern, 1981). If the gas pressure exceeds hydrostatic pressure, either by thermal pressuring or by burial overloading, the reservoir is said to 'overpressured' and is confined by a seal determined by lithostatic loading (Barker, 1987).

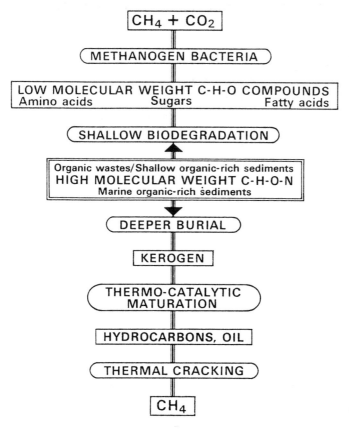

Figure 4 *The generation of subsurface methane*

Natural gases in the UK sector of the North Sea are generally 'dry', i.e. they contain mainly methane and low contents of higher molecular weight hydrocarbons. They comprise 90-95 % CH_4, about 5 % C_2-C_4 alkanes and about 2 % N_2, although the Hewett field, unusually in a Permo-Trias reservoir, is distinct in having about 8 % C_2-C_4 and 8 % N_2 (Barnard and Cooper, 1983).

3.2.4 Volcanic and other geological sources

In the UK, coal deposits, hydrocarbon reservoirs, marshes, peat and tidal sediments are the dominant geological sources of methane. In other regions of the world which are dynamically more active from a geological point of view, there are other possible geological sources of methane and associated gases (see, for example, MacDonald, 1983). These include volcanic, hydrothermal and geothermal settings; in igneous rocks and in fluid inclusions within minerals; methane hydrates in sea floor sediments; in faults, deep boreholes and formation waters; and some rarely observed occurrences of methane from abiogenic sources. These geological settings are summarised below and discussed in more detail in Appendix B.

1. Locations where acid and toxic gases (principally carbon dioxide, hydrogen sulphide and sulphur dioxide) arise from volcanic, hydrothermal and geothermal activities; combustible gases (hydrogen and methane) may be present but usually only as trace constituents; the dissolved acid gases can cause very acid groundwaters (pH as low as 1) in some areas.

2. Seismically active areas, e.g. Japan, California; where faults can act as conduits for gas migration; in the longer term, earthquake risks may outweigh those from gases.

3. Land sites in areas of uplifted oceanic crust (ophiolites) and low-temperature (20−150°C) hydrothermal activity can suffer from gas seeps rich in hydrogen and methane; the ultramafic (ferromagnesian) rocks suffer alteration reactions under such reducing conditions that these gases are evolved; such gas seeps have been observed in Oman, the Philippines and New Zealand.

4. Metamorphic rocks rich in vein mineralisation; although it is difficult to quantify the likely concentrations of methane present as fluid inclusions in mineral veins, it is possible that where veining is sufficiently intense, dangerous quantities of methane might be liberated during rock removing operations such as mining and tunnelling.

5. Where permafrost conditions maintain methane or natural gas hydrates at depths of 100 m or more in the ground; drilling operations in Alaska, Northern Canada or Siberia, for example, can release hydrocarbon gases by depressurisation.

6. Off-shore operations in waters deeper than about 300 m, corresponding to continental slopes, may encounter methane hydrates in the sea-floor sediments; these clathrate compounds evolve methane gas when depressurised or heated.

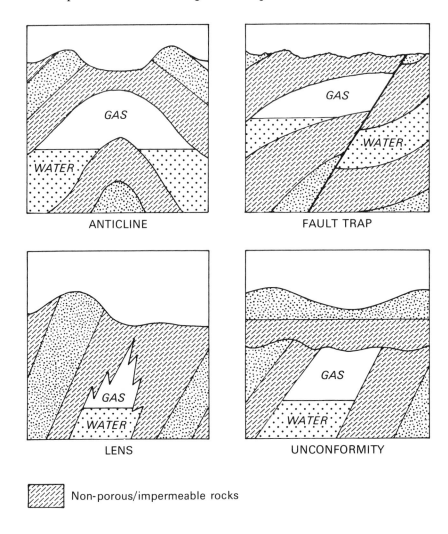

Non-porous/impermeable rocks

Figure 5 *Geological traps of gas*

3.3 BACTERIOGENIC SOURCES OF METHANE

Biological agents are the principal source of atmospheric methane release. Table 1 lists the amounts of methane produced per year from various bacteriogenic and anthropogenic sources.

The latter include emissions of methane from the world's coal mines, which coupled with natural gas leakages probably account for less than 10 % of global atmospheric methane (Creedy, 1989).

Methane is formed in large quantities as a result of the microbial decay of organic material in the absence of free oxygen i.e. under anaerobic conditions. Bacteria which produce methane, the 'methanogens', are strict anaerobes and can only thrive in the absence of free oxygen and in the presence of a suitable reducing agent. These are the terminal organisms in the microbial food chain, methane being one end-product of the anaerobic bacterial decomposition of organic matter (Ehrlich, 1981). They are very important in nature but are relatively difficult to isolate and maintain as pure cultures and for this reason have not been extensively studied.

Methanogens exist in many environments, from the rumen of cows to peat bogs, dung heaps, paddy fields, swamps and marshes, freshwater lakes, marine sediments, landfills, and organically contaminated groundwater; recently they have been isolated from dental plaque in humans (Rice and Claypool, 1981).

The methanogens are very specialised in that they produce methane and carbon dioxide as the major products from a limited range of relatively simple organic substrates: they have not been reported to utilise the larger molecular weight carbohydrates or amino acids. Doelle (1975) described three categories of compounds these bacteria can utilise, each species being restricted to the use of only a few compounds out of one or more category:

— lower fatty acids containing from 1 to 6 carbon atoms (such as formic, acetic, propionic, butyric acids)

— normal and isoalcohols containing between 1 and 5 carbon atoms (methanol, ethanol, etc.)

— the inorganic gases hydrogen, carbon monoxide and carbon dioxide.

Apart from carbon monoxide, these substrates are generally produced from the gradual biodegradation of more complex compounds such as carbohydrates, proteins and lipids, via respectively soluble sugars, amino acids and fatty acids (see Figure 6). These processes occur in shallow environments as compared to the process of formation of oil and natural gas from the deep burial and heating of organic rich sediments (see Figure 3).

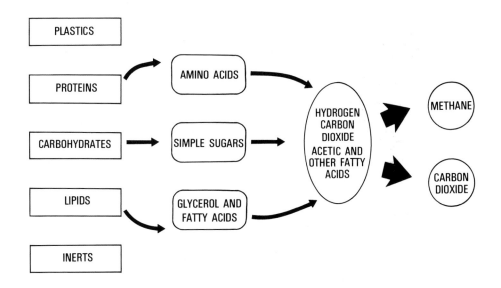

Figure 6 *Degradation sequences of organic materials*

This list of substrates can be simplified further since most authors believe that hydrogen and carbon dioxide or acetate are the preferred substrates with the only others utilised being formate, methanol and ethanol (Ehrlich, 1981; Rice and Claypool, 1981). The two most common processes by which methane is formed are:

Reduction of carbon dioxide:
$$CO_2 + 4H_2 \rightarrow CH_4 + 2H_2O$$

Methyl group reduction during the assimilation of acetate, i.e. acetate fermentation:
$$CH_3COO^- + H^+ \rightarrow CH_4 + CO_2.$$

Specific growth rates of the methanogens depend upon the species present, substrate, pH, redox potential (Eh), nutritional requirements and the presence of growth-inhibitory or growth-stimulatory substances. If a habitat is rich in biodegradable organic material, a nitrogen source and other essential elements but lacks oxygen, then an anaerobic microbial population will develop that may contain methanogenic bacteria. If high concentrations of sulphate or oxidised nitrogen compounds are present, different anaerobes will develop which under these conditions will have a selective advantage over the methanogens.

Other environmental requirements of methanogens are temperatures between 0°C and 75°C (the optimum for a specific population however is confined to a smaller range); a low redox potential of -200 to -300 mV; pH 6.7 to 7.4; and organic matter with greater than 0.5% organic carbon to act as a substrate (Rice and Claypool, 1981). For a detailed explanation of methanogenic bacteria and methanogenesis the reader is referred to Large (1983). Many natural sources of organic carbon, as well as many man-made organics, may be utilised by bacteria with the production of methane, carbon dioxide, and water.

There are three basic types of habitat that involve the production (and in some cases the consumption) of methane. These have been classified by Wolfe and Higgins (1979) as Type A habitats which include aquatic sediments, wetlands and anaerobic digesters, Type B habitats which include gastrointestinal habitats and Type C which includes habitats such as geothermal springs.

3.3.1 Landfill

Landfill practices currently account for the disposal of around 90% of UK refuse, approximately 26 million tonnes per year (ETSU, 1988). Over 50% of this refuse is composed of organic material including bovine waste, sewage sludge, urban refuse and agricultural residues, which are potentially degradable. Modern trends have encouraged the development of large, deep landfills in which the refuse can be densely packed and where conditions encourage the exclusion of air from much of the site. The microbiological processes which degrade organic matter in the absence of oxygen are therefore important in landfill sites. Such processes are commonly known as 'anaerobic digestion' and are similar to the processes described above for other, natural methane-producing environments such as marshes and swamps. In landfill sites the consequence of anaerobic digestion is the production of a methane-rich biogas, commonly called landfill gas, which is mainly composed of methane and carbon dioxide.

In theory, yields of around 400 m^3 of landfill gas per tonne of refuse input are possible (ETSU, 1988). This gas may contain 50% to 60% methane. In practice, yields are much lower than the theoretical values due to the conditions for anaerobic digestion being less than optimal in the landfill. Yields ranging from 50 to 250 m^3 per tonne of refuse over ten year periods are more commonly reported.

Waste characteristics

Organic wastes are generated in a number of ways, for example sewage, food processing effluent, animal slurry and domestic refuse. Unlike other wastes, domestic refuse has a very high solids content. The composition of waste is variable both within a waste source (for example different types of agricultural waste) and between different waste sources (see Figure 7).

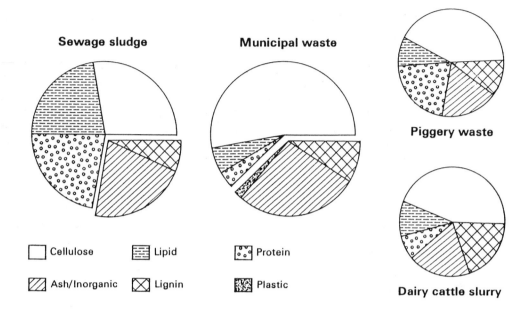

Figure 7 *Compositions of various waste types (after ETSU, 1988)*

The composition of a waste has a major influence on its degradation because the waste supplies the nutrients required for microbial growth and metabolism. The chemical composition and physical nature of waste will therefore influence the microbial ecology of waste degradation and the rate of production of the end-product, landfill gas. The variability of refuse composition will affect its rate of degradation and production of landfill gas. The nature of refuse has changed over the last 50 years, (ETSU, 1988) most noticeably through an increase in the proportion of paper in refuse, the introduction of plastics and a decrease in the proportion of ash (see Figures 8 and 9).

Although landfill microbiology and biochemistry are not directly analogous to other anaerobic systems, e.g. the rumen, sewage sludge, sediments and industrial anaerobic digesters, the general processes involved in anaerobic digestion are also involved in landfill waste degradation.

Waste degradation processes

The major metabolic steps in the anaerobic degradation of organic waste are shown in Figure 10. The dominant biodegradable material in landfills is carbohydrate (59%) with smaller amounts of lipids, i.e. fats and oils (5.7%) and proteins (2.7%). These are broken down by the processes of hydrolysis and acidogenesis into smaller molecular weight groups such as short chain fatty acids, amino acids and aliphatic alcohols. Methanogenic breakdown of these fatty acids requires an acetogenic species which produces acetic acid, hydrogen and carbon dioxide; this process occurs so long as these products are removed by the methanogens immediately. Detailed analyses of anaerobic digestion processes for refuse are given in ETSU (1988) and Senior (1990). The underlying theme in each process is the conversion of organic material to volatile fatty acids and its subsequent conversion to methane and carbon dioxide.

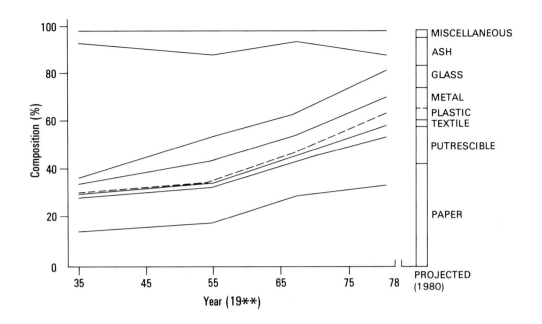

Figure 8 *Changes in refuse composition in the U.K. 1935 to 1980 (after ETSU, 1988)*

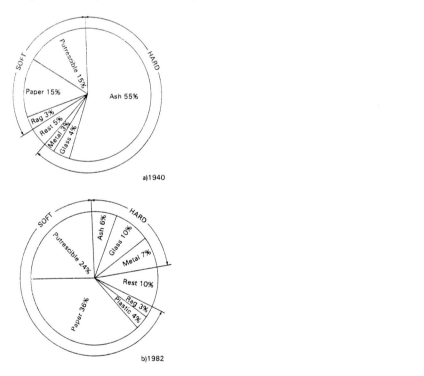

Figure 9 *Constituents of domestic refuse 1940 and 1982 (after Leach and Goodger, 1991)*

The theoretical pattern of biochemical events which occur in landfills is shown in Figure 11 and divides refuse stabilisation into five distinct phases within the overall process. These are, in order of event:

1. An aerobic phase involving oxygen depletion and temperature increase through aerobic respiration.

2. The establishment of anaerobic conditions and the evolution of carbon dioxide and hydrogen through acidogenic activity.

3. Commencement of methanogenic activity, the establishment of populations of methanogenic bacteria.

4. A phase of stable methanogenic activity.

5. A phase of decreasing methanogenic activity, representing substrate depletion and a return to aerobic conditions.

The pattern of events described assumes that upon placement oxygen is readily removed from the refuse and that refuse composition, bioavailability, pH, temperature, moisture (whether from infiltration of rainwater or of groundwater) and microflora are optimal for the generation of methane. Such a situation is rarely achieved in a landfill, but with increasing awareness of the potential use for methane as an energy source, landfill practices which aim to contain refuse, control water infiltration and minimise leachate generation should improve conditions for methane generation in landfill. It should be emphasised that the timing and duration of these phases can be variable and difficult to predict, and that chemical and physical conditions and refuse composition can differ enormously in different sites.

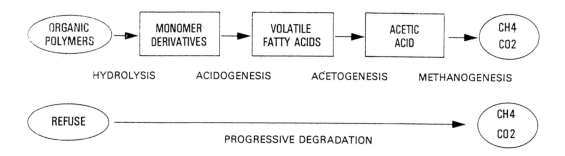

Figure 10 *Major degradative steps involved in the conversion of organic matter to methane and carbon dioxide during anaerobic digestion*

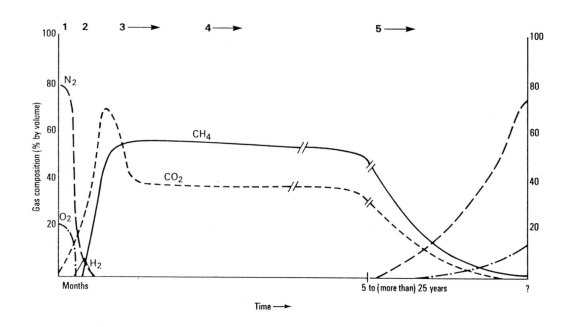

Figure 11 *Landfill gas composition profile with time (after Lawson and Alston, 1989)*

Williams and Harrison (1983) have developed an analytical model to estimate the production of landfill gas. The production of gas with time in a gradually saturating landfill based on a first-order degradation rate for the organic carbon in leachate was modelled using a number of estimated parameters including the rate of water rise, the initial total organic carbon (TOC) content, the rate of decay of TOC and the height of waste saturation. The water level in the landfill was assumed to rise at a given rate from its base, and only gas-production rates from the saturated refuse were calculated. The model indicates that a peak of gas production will occur and that gas production may continue to occur for tens of years after this peak has passed (see Figure 12). The model does not take into account gas production from the unsaturated part of the refuse, but Williams and Aitkenhead (1991) indicated that the background production of gas from the unsaturated refuse would not change the shape of the curve significantly but simply raise it. It was concluded that although the values obtained should not be taken as absolute rates of gas production, water penetration is a key factor in controlling the production of gas and on the timing of the peak-rate of gas generation.

3.3.2 Marine and lacustrine sediments

Sedimentary environments in which organic matter is deposited at a rate exceeding the supply of dissolved oxygen are characterised by anaerobic conditions. In recent sediments, methane is one end-product of the anaerobic bacterial decomposition of organic matter. Methane production in surface environments such as marshes is easily detectable because of its proximity to the surface. The conditions necessary for the growth of methanogenic bacteria have been described in the previous sections. They are strict anaerobes and will not grow even in the presence of trace concentrations of oxygen.

Furthermore, there is evidence that the methanogens do not grow in the presence of dissolved sulphate. At shallow depths within marine sediments bacterial methane production does not usually occur unless dissolved sulphate is almost completely removed from the interstitial water (Kaplan, 1974). In deep-sea sediments, the stage of complete removal of dissolved sulphate does not occur until burial depths of the order of tens of metres have been reached.

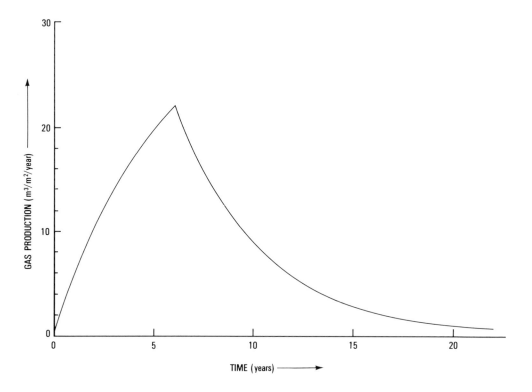

Figure 12 *Gas production from waste in a gradually saturating landfill as a function of time (after Williams and Harrison, 1983)*

The metabolic processes enabling microbes to obtain energy for growth and cell maintenance yield different amounts of energy, which along with environmental constraints, determine the nature of the microbial population. In a sediment, an ecological succession of metabolic processes becomes established with time and depth in the sedimentary column, with less efficient organisms being present at greater depths. Figure 13 shows three distinct biochemical environments which are each characterised by a dominant metabolic process: the aerobic zone, the sulphate-reducing zone and the carbonate-reduction or methanogenic zone. When such an ecological sequence is established, the zones move upward with time as sediment is added at the water-sediment interface or as the sediment moves downward in response to changing diagenetic or burial conditions.

When the sulphate concentration of the sediment pore water is low, as in brackish or freshwater environments and marine sediments below the sulphate-reducing zone, where sulphate has been removed from the pore waters by reduction, methane production becomes significant (Claypool and Kvenvolden, 1983). Substrates utilised by methanogenic bacteria have already been discussed (i.e. carbon dioxide and hydrogen or acetate are the preferred substrates).

Recently, on the North Sea bed, 'pock marks' have been observed which are believed to be an expression of natural gas emanation from the sea bed (Hovland and Judd, 1988). Seismic studies indicate that natural gas associated with traps below the surface is migrating along faults and escaping at the surface. The pock marks have so far been observed only in soft silty clays. This is probably because these sediments form a more plastic seal to the gas than sediments such as sand. The pock marks are being studied by the British Geological Survey and the Plymouth Marine Laboratory.

The occurrence of methane in marine and lacustrine sediments is widespread, and many studies are available in the literature e.g. Claypool and Kaplan (1974); Martens and Berner (1977); Oremland and Taylor (1978); Reeburgh (1980); Iversen and Jørgensen (1985); Jenden and Kaplan (1986); Sweeney (1988). It should be noted that sedimentation and accumulation of organic-rich matter can also occur in man-made reservoirs.

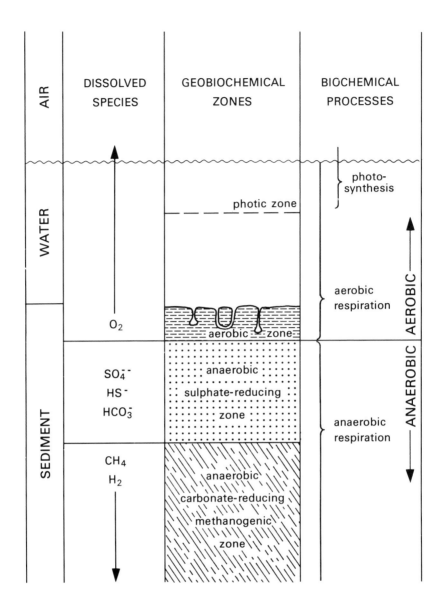

Figure 13 *An idealised cross-section of an organic-rich sedimentary environment with associated processes (after Kaplan, 1974)*

3.3.3 Wetland environments

Wetland environments include marshes, swamps, peatlands, lakes, man-made reservoirs, estuaries and rice paddies and are present in tropical, temperate and arctic climates. Releases of methane from wetland environments into the atmosphere (see Table 1) are considered to be the largest natural source of methane (Quay *et al.*, 1988).

The processes involved in the degradation of organic matter under anaerobic conditions to produce methane have been discussed in the previous sections. In wetland environments, biochemical and geochemical processes are initiated following the accumulation of plant debris and organic matter. Mechanical breakage and compaction occur. At the surface these changes take place under oxidising conditions, and after coverage by additional plant material and/or sediments and/or stagnant water, reducing, anaerobic conditions prevail. Under these reducing conditions the carbohydrates and proteins are further degraded to produce substrates utilisable by the methanogens, i.e. formate etc, carbon dioxide and acetate. Factors controlling methane emissions from wetland environments include temperature, oxygen concentration, water-table level, and the input rate and type of organic matter (Crill *et al.*, 1988).

Marshy or peaty environments usually produce a gas predominantly composed of methane and carbon dioxide. In a study of the composition of gases from freshwater and brackish water environments, Swain (1986) found 50% to 85% methane, 4% to 15% carbon dioxide and small or trace amounts of hydrogen, carbon monoxide, hydrogen sulphide and light hydrocarbons. The production of methane from wetland environments is well documented, e.g. Cicerone and Oremland (1988); Harriss *et al.* (1988); Chanton *et al.* (1988).

3.4 OTHER SOURCES OF METHANE AND ASSOCIATED GASES

Methane production is ubiquitous in nature since it is formed predominantly as an end-product of the anaerobic degradation of organic matter. In addition to those described in the previous sections, many other sources or potential sources of methane (and associated gases including carbon dioxide, carbon monoxide, hydrogen sulphide and hydrogen where applicable) can be listed.

Foundry sands at source frequently contain organic materials resulting from the foundry process such as phenolic binders, dextrin and coal dust, and in addition will often contain other general foundry wastes of a potentially gas-generating nature such as wood, rags and paper. These organic materials can provide substrates for methanogenic bacteria over the large surface areas offered by the sand grains. Foundry sands are encountered, for example, in the West Midlands, both as a constituent of mixed fills formerly deposited as wastes and as screened and sorted engineered fill. Where unscreened and deposited as a waste, foundry sands have been shown to generate methane at concentrations of up to 50 volume %, but as the corresponding emission rates and pressures tend to be low, the actual amount of gas is characteristically small. Gas flow rates and pressures within screened and compacted foundry sands are generally extremely low.

Deposits of sewage sludge which have not been effectively treated at sewage treatment works are often co-disposed in landfill sites or on sites adjacent to the works. Since the sludge consists of a large proportion of organic material it is possible that further degradation may occur to produce methane and carbon dioxide.

Certain types of refuse (e.g. building material) are often called inert but most types of material may be degraded by microbes or react in some way with other refuse; refuse containing gypsum or plasterboard may be degraded by sulphate-reducing bacteria to produce hydrogen sulphide under anaerobic conditions. Building materials, such as clayboard, timber and paper, are composed of organic material (cellulose) and under anaerobic conditions may be degraded to produce methane and carbon dioxide. Clayboard, which is widely used under foundations and slabs built on clay, has recently been reported to have produced methane and carbon dioxide in office blocks in central London and at the Oval cricket ground; the Building Research Establishment is investigating the problem (Fowler, 1991).

Leaks from underground fuel tanks and pipelines, gas mains leaks, fuel spillages, the dumping of solvents or hydrocarbon wastes or the degradation of man-made organic pollutants from petrol refineries or garages may lead to gas production on reclaimed (or other) land. Gas chromatographic techniques may help to identify the source of the gas.

Gases may be generated by chemical reactions between deposited chemicals and groundwater, e.g. unregulated drums containing volatile organic compounds, acid or alkaline leachate, or liquors. For example, calcium sulphide reacts with acid to give hydrogen sulphide and cyanides react with acids to give hydrogen cyanide.

The number of situations where the conditions necessary for methane and carbon dioxide production from the anaerobic degradation of organic matter is enormous. Some of the situations most likely to be encountered are listed below:

— compost heaps

— fly tipping

— cemeteries

— buried farm animal carcasses

— farmyard dung heaps

— old cess pits

— in tropical and sub-tropical climates, termite hills

— flatulence and eructations of animals (especially cattle, sheep, goats, deer and horses).

In addition to the degradation of organic matter, carbon dioxide is produced as a by-product of fires, explosions, blasting, internal combustion engines and the effect of acids on carbonate minerals and rocks.

Carbon monoxide is a common constituent of blasting fumes and may be produced by poorly maintained engines and overheated air compressors.

Hydrogen sulphide is produced by the decomposition of organic matter which contains sulphur and is thus commonly found in the vicinity of landfill sites and sewage treatment works. It may also be produced in landfill sites which contain sulphate-rich waste such as plasterboard. It is also common where acid mine water reacts with sulphide minerals such as iron pyrites. It is a well known contaminant of paper mill sites, oil refineries, coal carbonisation sites and chemical works.

Hydrogen is formed by fermentation processes (as in the early stage of a landfill evolution), corrosion processes (e.g. steel borehole casings in the ground), during battery charging and in fires at temperatures greater than 250°C. After methane explosions hydrogen is present in similar quantities to carbon monoxide (Edwards, 1989).

4 Methane source identification

The gas explosions at Loscoe and Abbeystead have highlighted the dangers associated with the migration of methane in the subsurface, and the need to establish quickly and accurately the source of the methane in order to instigate appropriate measures for control and remediation (Williams and Aitkenhead, 1989 and 1991; DoE, 1986).

Methane can form in a large number of different environments or geological strata including coal seams, hydrocarbon deposits, sediments, soils, groundwaters and landfills. As a result it may be difficult to distinguish the source of a particular methane sample. Stable isotope ratio studies, the identification of associated gases in a methane-containing gas mixture and radiocarbon dating techniques are the most widely used methods for methane source identification. The importance of the integration of geological, geochemical and hydrogeological information when attempting to identify a methane source should be stressed.

4.1 BASIS OF SOURCE IDENTIFICATION

In several instances where methane has been detected in the vicinity of landflls, the landfll has not been necessarily the only methane source; leaking gas mains, sewers, indigenous gas from underlying Carboniferous strata, and the products of anaerobic degradation of organically contaminated groundwater are all possible sources of methane.

To confirm a methane source three approaches may be used. The source can be identifed by comparing the composition of the gas mixture with known source compositions; identifying a migration pathway between the putative source and the point at which methane is observed; and confirming the existence of a driving force (such as diffusion or convection; see Section 6) capable of moving the gas along the pathway (Williams and Hitchman, 1989). In the last case it may also be necessary to assess the potential for compositional changes such as oxidation or reduction processes during migration. In most cases, only the first approach is taken, usually by comparing major and trace components with those of known gases, or by determining the radiocarbon content to distinguish 'geological' from recent biogenic methane. If more than one source of methane exists, identification may be difficult.

4.2 ASSOCIATED GASES

The gases associated with methane can be diagnostic of the methane source. The compositions of various methane-containing gases are shown in Table 6. Such compositions form the general basis for source discrimination.

Landfill gas usually contains a variety of volatile organic compounds (DoE, 1986), but may require specialised sampling equipment for collection (Brookes and Young, 1983). A theoretical representation of the proportions of various gases which may be produced during the life-time of a landfill is described in Section 3.3.1 and illustrated in Figure 11.

Where compositional evidence alone is used it is important to have a well defned database, and to consider possible changes in composition that may have occurred during migration. For instance the CH_4: CO_2 ratio is often used in source identification, especially for landfill gas (Emberton, 1984). However, carbon dioxide may be 'filtered out' during migration, e.g. by sorption on wet incinerator ash, or may undergo chromatographic separation in moving through a suitable fine-grained sediment or soil. The solubility of carbon dioxide means that it may be easily removed by solution in groundwater or by precipitation as carbonate mineral. Similarly, methane is known to be oxidised to carbon dioxide by bacteria, which can make CH_4: CO_2 ratios unreliable for source determination.

Natural gas of thermogenic origin has a larger percentage of heavy hydrocarbons, lower amounts of nitrogen and carbon dioxide, and a smaller ethane:propane ratio (Mogilevsky, 1964). These factors can be useful in identifying the origin of the gas, but isotopes provide a much more consistent method.

4.3 RADIOCARBON CHARACTERISATION OF METHANE

Methane may be characterised radiometrically by its radiocarbon (^{14}C) content, or isotopically by the ratio between its stable isotopes of carbon ($^{12}C/^{13}C$) and hydrogen ($^{2}H/^{1}H$) (see Appendix C). Radiocarbon analysis is based on the fact that all living organisms contain the radioactive isotope of carbon which is produced naturally in the upper atmosphere by the cosmic ray bombardment of nitrogen atoms. It has also been created as a result of atmospheric thermonuclear testing. Modern organisms contain relatively abundant ^{14}C which, when the organism dies, decays to half its original activity after 5 730 years. Hence landfill gas produced from recent vegetable matter can easily be distinguished from mine gas which is so old (350 million years) that all its original radiocarbon will have decayed.

Where natural gas or mine gas source is suspected, radiocarbon measurements can be used to determine the apparent age of the methane. The ^{14}C isotope emits beta-radiation at a relatively low energy (156 keV) and as natural activities are low, highly effcient sophisticated detection equipment is needed. The methane is first combusted to carbon dioxide, then either (in most cases) synthesised to benzene for liquid scintillation counting, or (when samples are small) purifed for gas proportional counting (Bowen, 1988). While this is a very useful technique, it can be expensive and may take considerable time to carry out.

4.4 USE OF ISOTOPES IN DETERMINING THE PROVENANCE OF METHANE

The proportion of the non-radioactive or stable isotopes of carbon (^{12}C to ^{13}C) and of hydrogen (deuterium/hydrogen) may be diagnostic of various sources of methane and these appear to offer a cheaper method of identification under certain conditions. The application of the technique is presently being investigated by the British Geological Survey (Hitchman *et al.*, 1989).

The theoretical basis behind the use of isotope studies in determining the origin of methane is discussed in detail in Appendix C. For carbon isotope studies, the ^{12}C to ^{13}C isotope ratio in a sample is compared with a known ^{12}C to ^{13}C ratio in an internationally used standard. If the sample is enriched in the heavy ^{13}C isotope compared with the standard, it has a positive $\delta^{13}C$ value and its isotopic composition is described as 'heavy' compared to the standard. The greater the enrichment in ^{13}C the larger the $\delta^{13}C$ value. If the sample is depleted in the heavy ^{13}C isotope relative to the standard then it is enriched in ^{12}C and has a negative $\delta^{13}C$ value; the isotopic composition of the sample is described as 'light' relative to the standard. This concept is illustrated in Figure 14. The isotopic ratios of different samples can be compared and used to infer the different processes involved in their formation. For example, methane produced by the anaerobic microbial degradation of organic matter has been shown to be enriched in ^{12}C relative to thermogenic methane.

A great deal of research has been carried out in order to distinguish the sources of economic deposits of natural gas, specifically methane. According to Jenden and Kaplan (1986), $C_{2+}: C_{total}$ hydrocarbon ratios less than 0.01, together with $\delta^{13}C_{CH4}$ values more negative than minus 55 ‰, are good evidence that a natural gas accumulation is bacteriogenic rather than thermogenic in origin. However, the concentration of C_{2+} hydrocarbons (those hydrocarbon molecules containing two or more carbon atoms) is not a reliable indicator for distinguishing between the two gas origins. Little is known about the generation of C_{2+} hydrocarbons and their concentrations may vary; also, thermogenic gas generated from certain types of organic matter may have very low C_{2+} hydrocarbon contents. It is also possible that C_{2+} hydrocarbons may be lost from thermogenic gas during near-surface migration, due to adsorption onto sedimentary organic matter or to chromatographic separation.

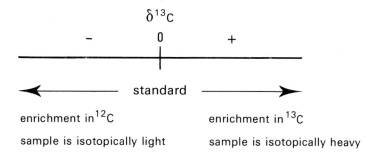

Figure 14 *Variation in carbon isotope composition*

The source identification of methane from other environments has been the subject of much research. Barker and Fritz (1981a), seeing the wide variety of environments from which methane is produced − lakes, oceans, soils, sediments, coal seams, hydrocarbon reservoirs, landfills, fluid inclusions, volcanic gases and groundwaters − realised the importance of identifying whether the gas in each case is produced by biochemical or non-biochemical processes. They used the carbon isotope ratio of the methane to define its origin, the most negative $\delta^{13}C$ values indicating low temperature environments, i.e. a bacteriogenic origin; and higher (less negative) $\delta^{13}C$ values indicating higher temperature environments and thus a thermogenic origin.

Barker and Fritz (1981a) pointed out that methanogenic bacteria produce methane which is depleted in ^{13}C by 25-75 ‰ relative to the carbon substrate, whereas laboratory cracking experiments at 350-600°C yielded thermogenic methane depleted in ^{13}C by less than 30 ‰ relative to the parent organic substrate. This depletion of biogenic methane in ^{13}C relative to thermogenic methane is a result of different isotopic fractionation between the source carbon and the methane in the two processes. Bottinga (1969) showed that the equilibrium fractionation factor for CO_2-CH_4 increased from about 1.03 at 200°C to about 1.08 at 0°C. This means that at equilibrium, methane will be about 77 ‰ 'lighter' than the substrate at 0°C and only about 33 ‰ lighter than the substrate at 200°C. Although carbon isotopic equilibrium is rarely attained in nature, it is frequently approached, and the difference in temperature of formation is a valid explanation for the isotopic differences observed between bacteriogenic and thermogenic methane.

Schoell (1980; 1983) concentrated on the combined changes in both carbon and hydrogen isotopes in his aims to determine the origin of methane. He agreed with the general ideas already mentioned, namely that bacteriogenic gases are devoid of most C_2 to C_4 hydrocarbons and are depleted in ^{13}C. Schoell also recognised common trends in the hydrogen isotope compositions: distinct fractionations exist when methane is formed by microbial processes. The deuterium concentrations of bacteriogenic methane from world-wide occurrences vary with δD ranging from −170 to −280 ‰. They are all generally about 160 ‰ less (lighter) than the deuterium concentrations of their associated waters. Theoretical considerations support this relationship with the idea that the hydrogen in the waters has been used by bacteria in effecting the reduction of carbon dioxide to form methane. Methane gases of terrestrial origin have more negative δD values than marine methane gases, due to differences in deuterium concentrations in the respective environmental waters (Schoell, 1980; 1983). Thermogenic gases, on the other hand, have δD values from −260 to −150 ‰, with deuterium contents increasing with decreasing wetness of the gas (Schoell, 1980). Dry gases which are not associated with petroleum show deuterium enrichment such that their δD values are generally in the range from −180 to −130 ‰.

The limitations of the use of the $\delta^{13}C_{CH4}$ value must, however, be realised. The $\delta^{13}C$ boundary between microbial and thermogenic methane has been arbitrarily assigned and athough a value of $-55\ ‰$ to $-60\ ‰$ is commonly cited, microbial methane less negative than $-55\ ‰$ has been reported from marine sediments, lacustrine sediments, marshes, landfills and sludge digestors (Hitchman et al., 1989).

Isotopic distinction between bacteriogenic and thermogenic methane may be complicated by such processes as microbial oxidation of methane leaving residual methane enriched in ^{13}C such that it is brought into the range associated with thermogenic methane. Also, landfill methane tends to be enriched in ^{13}C relative to most bacteriogenic methane (Games and Hayes, 1976; Barker and Fritz, 1981b), possibly due to higher rates of metabolism, organic substrate concentration and elevated temperatures. These physico-chemical conditions may result in less carbon isotope fractionation during methanogenesis.

In order to assess whether stable isotope ratios could be diagnostic of particular sources, Hitchman et al. (1989) collected and analysed methane containing gases from a variety of origins. These included coal fields, North Sea gas fields, landfills, anaerobic digesters and lake and river muds. The results were compared with those of previous studies in order to compile a database of the likely composition of possible source gases and to evaluate whether changes in composition may have occurred during gas migration. The results indicated that stable carbon and hydrogen isotope ratios in methane should be sufficient in most cases to identify its source. In cases where plotting δD_{CH4} against $\delta^{13}C_{CH4}$ is inconclusive, as it can be when distinguishing mine from landfill gas, the $\delta^{13}C_{CO2}$ value should provide the basis for differentiation.

In summary, stable isotope studies can aid in discriminating the various sources of methane which is formed by various processes in the Earths's crust. Basic evidence for the variety of these processes is provided by observations of methane formation in highly different environments with correspondingly large variations in isotopic signatures; isotope concentrations of methane are predominantly controlled by the processes of methane formation (Schoell, 1988). Isotope studies should ideally be augmented by other geochemical and hydrogeological information when making a positive identification of a methane source.

5 Geobiochemistry of methane

Methane is a labile gas which means that it is chemically and biochemically reactive. Methane can be oxidised both under aerobic conditions (in the presence of free oxygen) and under anaerobic conditions (in the absence of free oxygen) to form carbon dioxide. It is important to understand the geobiochemical processes affecting methane in the ground because the chemical by-products such as carbon dioxide and bicarbonate and the production of heat can have profound influences on the ground and groundwater. The presence of methane in the soil zone may result in distressed or dead vegetation as methane oxidation cycles are established depleting the oxygen supply in the soil and producing carbon dioxide and heat.

Methane may be aerobically oxidised usually in the unsaturated zone. There is a growing body of evidence to suggest that methane may be anaerobically oxidised in the saturated zone by bacterial processes. Stable isotope ratios have been used to study these oxidation processes and support the theory of microbial mediation during anaerobic methane oxidation, although the process is not fully understood. In water containing high methane concentrations, water chemistry is altered, and the process of methane oxidation adversely affects water quality.

5.1 AEROBIC METHANE OXIDATION

Aerobic methane oxidation occurs in the unsaturated zone of soils and sediments. Various types of methane oxidising bacteria have been identified (Panganiban *et al.*, 1979) which are known as Type 1 and Type 2 methylotrophs. These bacteria exist in the soil zone, in the top layers of marine sediments and in the unsaturated zone, and are most abundant where methane and oxygen are present (Zobell, 1964). It appears that carbon dioxide is needed to initiate growth, and that these bacteria are highly active in an atmosphere of 10 to 40% oxygen, up to 70% methane and 5-20% carbon dioxide (Doelle, 1975). The reaction sequence is as follows:

$$CH_4 \rightarrow CH_3OH \rightarrow HCHO \rightarrow HCOOH \rightarrow CO_2$$

methane   methanol   formaldehyde   formic acid   carbon dioxide

The overall reaction is:

$$CH_4 + 2O_2 \rightarrow CO_2 + 2H_2O + HEAT.$$

The reaction products, i.e. carbon dioxide and heat, can be useful indicators of the presence of methane. The production of heat offers a means of detecting the presence of soil methane by thermographic or thermal imaging techniques (see Crowhurst and Manchester, 1992).

The effects of aerobic methane oxidation were highlighted during investigations following the gas explosion at Loscoe (see Section 7.4 and Williams and Aitkenhead, 1991). In the 2 to 3 years prior to the explosion there had been several reports of distressed vegetation in gardens in the area. Typically the soil had become warm and crumbled and vegetation had died. Boreholes drilled after the explosion showed that an increase in temperature from 18°C at 2.5 m to about 21°C at 0.5 m below the surface was mirrored by a decrease in methane concentration (see Figure 15). The patterns of methane concentration and temperature were consistent with the theory that methane migrating to the surface was being oxidised, possibly by bacteria, in the soil zone. The gas below the zone of oxidation was similar in composition to landfill gas, consisting of about 60% methane and 40% carbon dioxide (see Figure 15). Much of the methane that is produced in water-logged soils, paddy fields and sphagnum bogs is oxidised in the surface of the soil by methane oxidising bacteria.

Heating effects due to methane oxidation in the soil zone probably follow a cyclic pattern. Initially, methane migrates upwards through the soil over a given area. Bacteria common in soils, such as *Pseudomonas methanica* utilise and oxidise methane with the evolution of heat, water vapour and carbon dioxide. The depletion of the oxygen supply and the generation of heat are thought to limit the growth or cause the death of vegetation.

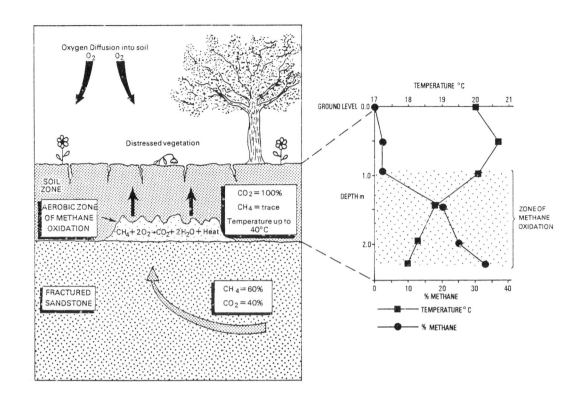

Figure 15 *Aerobic oxidation of methane in the soil zone (after Williams and Aitkenhead, 1991)*

Since the heat causes a net loss of moisture from the soil, desiccation cracks develop. The gas then migrates preferentially through these cracks to the surface, by-passing the active microbial zone where oxidation occurs. The temperature consequently falls and high methane concentrations appear near the surface. If the soil weathers, the desiccation cracks could seal up and the methane could again invade the soil zone, possibly in adjacent areas, to repeat the cycle.

5.2 ANAEROBIC METHANE OXIDATION

In addition to aerobic oxidation of methane there is a substantial and growing volume of evidence in support of the oxidation of methane under anaerobic conditions (Reeburgh, 1976, 1980; Devol and Ahmed, 1981; Devol, 1983; Alperin *et al.*, 1988). However, microbiologists have not yet managed to isolate a specific organism or microbial consortium which facilitates the reaction and have not proved how the reaction proceeds. Much of the research into anaerobic methane oxidation, which appears to occur in the saturated zone, has been carried out in anoxic (oxygen depleted) marine sediments where there is a zonation of different redox (reduction-oxidation) reactions and their associated potentials with depth in the sediment. A sulphate-reducing zone is often present above the methanogenic zone. It has been suggested that during methane diffusion into this sulphate zone, sulphate-respiring bacteria anaerobically oxidise methane while reducing the sulphate (Reeburgh, 1980). Furthermore, the methane concentration is found to be low at the sediment surface but to increase with depth, while sulphate concentrations are the reverse (see Figure 16). A drop in the methane concentration profile occurs at the boundary between the methanogenic and sulphate-reduction zones, suggesting that sulphate reduction is directly or indirectly coupled with methane oxidation. The reaction is thermodynamically possible (Alperin and Reeburgh, 1984) and may be written:

$$CH_4 + SO_4^{2-} \rightarrow HCO_3^- + HS^- + H_2O.$$

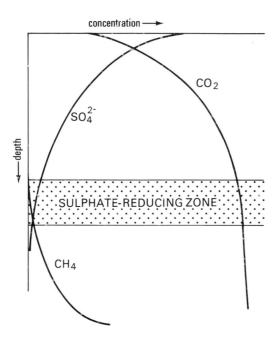

Figure 16 *Depth profiles of concentrations of methane, sulphate and carbon dioxide with respect to anaerobic methane oxidation*

In a study into the origin of Jurassic carbonate concretions containing diagenetic pyrite (FeS_2), evidence for the involvement of anaerobic methane oxidation and sulphate reduction in the concretionary growths was provided by sulphur stable isotope and chemical observations (Raiswell, 1988). The pyrite was deposited as a result of the reaction between iron in the sediment and the hydrogen sulphide (H_2S) produced by microbial sulphate reduction. The pyrite was precipitated simultaneously with the carbonate. Carbonate can be precipitated by generation from sedimentary organic matter or, theoretically, during the microbially mediated oxidation of methane. Since there was no evidence to indicate the presence of a local source of organic material, it was concluded that the carbonate was in fact derived from the microbially mediated sulphate reduction/methane oxidation process. The concretions, therefore, provided further evidence in support of anaerobic methane oxidation processes.

Evidence for the modern occurrence of anaerobic methane oxidation has been found at the Villa Farm Research Site, near Coventry (Williams, 1988). An extensive pollution plume has developed in a shallow sand aquifer following the discharge of liquid wastes into a lagoon. Methane production has been confirmed at the base of the aquifer, but a soil gas survey in the zone immediately above the water table revealed predominantly carbon dioxide and only traces of methane, except for an area at the leading edge of the plume where it was relatively thin and depleted in sulphate. It appears that methane is being produced in the heavily contaminated zone at the base of the aquifer, but that it is being utilised in some way, probably by sulphate reducing bacteria, and that it is being oxidised, *in situ*, to carbon dioxide.

5.3 EFFECTS OF METHANE OXIDATION ON GROUNDWATER QUALITY AND CHEMISTRY

Redox reactions which occur in groundwater, e.g. aerobic respiration, nitrate reduction, sulphate reduction and carbonate reduction, are important because the elements in groundwater form different compounds depending on whether they are under predominantly reducing or oxidising conditions. The chemical analysis of groundwater is therefore necessary for establishing the series of redox reactions which are occurring. This, in turn, can indicate whether the conditions for methane production or methane oxidation are present in the water.

A redox reaction is one comprising a simultaneous oxidation and reduction reaction. The substance which is reduced is defined as an electron acceptor (oxidising agent), and the substance which is oxidised as an electron donor (reducing agent). Since there are no free electrons, every oxidation reaction is accompanied by a reduction reaction. The redox potential, Eh, of a groundwater is a measure of its oxidising or reducing capacity. Eh is measured in mV; large positive values indicate oxidising conditions; large negative values indicate the prevalence of strongly reducing conditions. The Eh value is obtained for a redox reaction written as a reduction equation or electron acceptance process (see example equations below) through the Nernst equation:

$$ Eh = E° + \frac{2.3RT}{(nF)} \log_{10} \left[\frac{reactants}{products} \right] $$

where $E°$ is the standard potential (mV), R the gas constant, T the absolute temperature, F the Faraday constant, n the number of electrons transferred in the reaction, and the brackets refer to concentrations or, more accurately, activities of the redox species. $E°$ of a particular redox couple is measured relative to the standard potential of the hydrogen electrode, which is given the value zero. At 25°C, the $2.3RT/F$ term is equal to 59 mV/eq and the Nernst equation becomes:

$$ Eh = E° + \frac{59}{(nF)} \log_{10} \left[\frac{reactants}{products} \right] $$

Champ *et al.* (1979) proposed a sequence of redox reactions (see Table 4) which are likely to occur within an aquifer, based on the thermodynamic principles outlined by Stumm and Morgan (1970).

Table 4 Eh values of some reduction reactions

Reaction			Eh (mV)*	
$^1/_4O_2 + H^+ + e$	=	$^1/_2H_2O$	+ 813	(1)
$^1/_5NO_3^- + ^6/_5 H^+ + e^-$	=	$^1/_{10}N_2 + ^3/_5 H_2O$	+ 746	(2)
$^1/_2MnO_2 + 2H^+ + e^-$	=	$^1/_2Mn^{2+} + H_2O$	+ 396	(3)
$^1/_8NO_3^- + ^5/_4H^+ + e^-$	=	$^1/_8NH_4^+ + ^3/_8H_2O$	+ 363	(4)
$Fe(OH)_3 + 3H^+ + e^-$	=	$Fe^{2+} + 3H_2O$	− 185	(5)
$^1/_8CO_2 + H^+ + e^-$	=	$^1/_8HS^- + ^1/_2H_2O$	− 214	(6)
$^1/_8SO_4^{2-} + ^9/_8H^+ + e^-$	=	$^1/_8CH_4 + ^1/_4H_2O$	− 244	(7)
$^1/_6N_2 + ^4/_3H^+ + e$	=	$^1/_3NH_4^+$	− 277	(8)
$^1/_4CO_2 + H^+ + e^-$	=	$^1/_4CH_2O + ^1/_4H_2O$	− 484	(9)

* $Eh = E° + 59\log[H^+]^p$, where $[H^+] = 10^{-7}M$, i.e. pH 7, and p = stoichiometric coefficient for H^+.

Changes in the measured potential will be observed as the sequence of redox reactions proceeds. Natural waters that contain large quantities of oxidising agents, e.g. dissolved oxygen, give measurements of high Eh, while those containing large quantities of reducing agents, e.g. dissolved organic carbon (DOC), have low redox potentials. Water in solubility equilibrium with air at pH 7 and 25°C contains dissolved oxygen and has an Eh value of +813 mV which is large enough in theory to drive all the above reactions (2) to (9) to their left-hand sides. However, kinetic reasons often obstruct the attainment of these thermodynamic equilibria. Microbially produced enzymes naturally present in groundwaters can increase the rates of some of the reactions by acting as catalysts. Reactions can also be speeded by heterogeneous catalysis at mineral surfaces and by homogeneous catalysis involving complex ion formation. As the chemical reactions involved may not have reached equilibrium and may not be reversible (two of the major assumptions of the Nernst equation), the measured potential in groundwaters cannot be quantitatively correlated with the concentrations of dissolved species using thermodynamic principles. The redox potentials, therefore, only indicate overall qualitative changes in the aquifer, where the waters are in a dynamic rather than an equilibrium condition.

Champ *et al.* (1979) considered a closed groundwater system containing excess DOC, represented by CH_2O in reaction (9) above, which acts as a powerful reducing agent. In a confined aquifer the groundwater species will be reduced in the sequence oxygen, nitrate, Mn(IV), Fe(III), sulphate, bicarbonate and nitrogen. As the reactions proceed, the Eh will drop and become more negative and the amount of DOC should also decrease unless it is supplied from a dissolving solid phase of organic matter. The oxidation of the DOC creates the Eh conditions, i.e. anaerobic and reducing, for methanogenesis to take place. The microbially mediated production of methane in marshes, bogs, swamps, paddy fields and organic-rich sediments can be explained thermodynamically according to the simple reactions of (9) and (7) in Table 4. A useful discussion of thermodynamic controls upon microbial metabolism is given elsewhere (Claypool and Kaplan, 1974) applied to marine organic-rich sediments; if the sediments in tidal and marine areas contain more than 0.5% organic carbon and are being rapidly deposited, the maintenance of the anoxic conditions necessary for methanogenesis is assured and methane formation occurs.

In studies (Jones and Rauch, 1978; Beebe and Rauch, 1979) of water containing high methane concentrations, it was found that a correlation existed between the methane concentration and increased concentrations of nitrate and bicarbonate along with decreased concentrations of sulphate. A further study (Gunsalus *et al.*, 1972) of well water containing high methane concentrations showed the presence of relatively large concentrations of dissolved iron and manganese, high ammonium concentrations with respect to nitrate, no detectable sulphate and very high alkalinity (i.e. high bicarbonate content).

A study of the effects of the introduction of methane gas to near-surface groundwater subsequent to a gas well blow out in Madison, Ohio, (Kelly *et al.*, 1985) showed that recognisable changes in the groundwater chemistry had occurred. In water wells affected by methane infiltration elevated levels of sulphide and iron, manganese and calcium ion concentrations were found, alkalinity and pH values were increased and low levels of dissolved oxygen, sulphate and and nitrate were found relative to water wells uncontaminated by methane.

These changes were compared with thermodynamic predictions of equations (1 to 9) in Table 4 concerning the effects of the addition of methane to near-surface groundwaters. Thermodynamic considerations predicted the following changes:

(1) An increase in pH.

(2) A decrease in Eh.

(3) Production of alkalinity from methane oxidation (equation 7).

(4) Nearly complete reduction of sulphate to hydrogen sulphide (equation 6).

(5) Complete to nearly complete reduction of nitrate to ammonium (equation 4).

(6) Reduction of iron and manganese oxides, along with a consequent increase in their aqueous concentrations, and precipitation of iron and manganese carbonates and/or sulphides (equations 6 and 8).

(7) Readjustment of common cation (Na, K, Ca, Mg) concentrations to equilibria defined by their controlling ionic, complexation and mineral reactions.

The field data agreed qualitatively with most of the thermodynamic predictions. Alkalinity (due to the presence of bicarbonate), ammonium, iron and manganese ion concentrations were highest in wells affected by methane infiltration. Dissolved oxygen, nitrate, and sulphate concentrations were lower. The reduction of sulphate was the predominant alkalinity producing reaction related to the oxidation of methane.

Apart from any potential hazards created by the release of dissolved methane from near-surface waters, significant water chemistry changes have been shown to occur which affect the acceptable standard of water quality. The production of sulphides renders water unpalatable and the generation of finely disseminated sulphide minerals imparts a black colouration to water and can clog water supply wells. These effects could be accentuated in groundwaters having high levels of dissolved sulphate. The presence of iron and manganese can adversely affect the taste of potable water and stain plumbing fixtures.

5.4 EFFECTS OF METHANE OXIDATION ON ISOTOPIC RATIOS IN METHANE AND ASSOCIATED GASES

Geochemical studies of the stable isotope ratio compositions of methane and associated carbon dioxide can be very helpful in identifying their origin, providing a sensitive indicator of the biochemical or non-biochemical sources of methane and providing information on the oxidation processes affecting methane. The theory of stable isotope use and the isotopic fractionation that takes place during aerobic and anaerobic oxidation of methane are described in detail in Appendices C, D and E.

6 Migration of methane

The migration of gas in the ground is governed by a number of factors which are specific to the site or area of concern. For gas migration to occur there must be a driving force to move the gas and an available pathway. The pathway may exist by the nature of the geology or result from man-made disturbances to the ground or as a combination of these factors. The driving force for migration may be a concentration gradient resulting in diffusive gas flux or a pressure gradient resulting in viscous gas flux. Gases may also be transported in solution in groundwater.

The identification of gas migration pathways depends upon the gathering of detailed information on both the geology and hydrogeology of the area and on the location of man-made features of the ground. Where sufficient information is available it may be possible to apply mathematical models which predict the rates of gas migration.

An important point to remember is that the controls on the movement of methane and other gases or groundwater containing gases in solution may be recognised during a desk study and the site investigation phase prior to construction, but that circumstances during the construction and operation phases may change the controls governing the migration. At the design stage a forward assessment of *risk change* brought about by the construction process is advisable. In all civil engineering operations, especially underground works, the feedback of monitoring information to the engineer or operator should be an integral part of the project.

6.1 MIGRATION MECHANISMS

Gas may migrate through rocks if they are permeable and if there is a force acting to drive gas through them. Fluids may pass through the rock by movement through pore spaces between individual mineral grains as in unconsolidated sand and gravel. In more consolidated rocks, gas may flow through mechanical discontinuities such as fractures, joints, bedding and fault planes (Tomlinson, 1988; Stenhouse and Grogan, 1991).

Strong rocks such as crystalline rocks often have a higher permeability than weaker sediments such as mudstones, because their fractures are open and interconnected throughout the mass of the rock. In mudstones, fissures are closed and the ability to transmit fluids is limited. Diffusion of methane through intact coal is a relatively slow process, but in coal seams which are fractured and more permeable methane can diffuse at a faster rate (Thimons and Kissell, 1973). Gas or water permeability may be enhanced where rocks have been disturbed by natural processes such as landslipping, glacial action and faulting or as a result of mining subsidence or blasting during quarrying.

The gas permeability of a granular formation such as unfractured sandstone is roughly inversely proportional to its degree of saturation by a liquid; if the pores are filled with water, gas cannot move directly through the rock. The gas can only move as a result of slow diffusion through the water. Only when the rock becomes unsaturated so that there is a continuous gas-filled pathway through the rock will gas be able to flow to any significant extent. As the degree of saturation falls from this point, the gas permeability of the formation increases to a maximum when the rock is completely unsaturated. If the liquid phase is mobile, for example water percolating through a landfill or leachate migrating from a landfill, single-phase (gas) transport may be transformed to a two-phase flow phenomenon (Bear, 1972). Gases may also be transported in solution by groundwater where sufficiently high pressures exist and exsolved when the water pressure is reduced (see Section 6.5.4).

The movement of a gas through a porous medium can take place as a result of molecular diffusion due to a concentration gradient or as viscous flow due to a pressure gradient. Ghabaee and Rodwell (1989) found that experimental and computer simulation studies of multicomponent gas flow in porous media showed that both pressure driven (viscous) and diffusion fluxes contribute to the overall gas flux, and both should be taken into account in any detailed study of landfill (or other) gas flow. Figure 17 is a schematic representation of a number of processes and geological factors which may affect methane as it migrates through the ground.

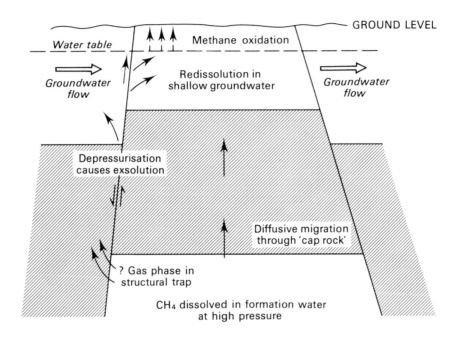

Figure 17 *Processes during the migration of methane*

6.1.1 Gas Diffusion

Gaseous diffusion is caused by the existence of a concentration gradient. Diffusion processes result from the Brownian motion of atoms or molecules in solids, liquids and gases. Diffusion is the process by which matter is transported from one part of a system to another as a result of random molecular motions. Since the rate of diffusion of a gas is inversely proportional to the square root of its density (Graham's Law, see Appendix F.1), a light gas such as methane will migrate more quickly than heavier gases such as carbon dioxide. Millington's equation (see Appendix F.2) relates the diffusion coefficient of a gas in air to that in a water-saturated or non water-saturated porous medium.

In 1855, Fick realised the similarity between heat conduction and gaseous diffusion and showed that the rate of gas diffusion through a unit cross-sectional area of a given porous medium is dependent upon the gas concentration gradient measured normal to the section. Fick's First and Second Laws are explained in Appendix F.3. Diffusion occurs more freely at higher temperatures; thus diffusion coefficients increase with temperature.

For diffusion through unsaturated porous media, Fick's Law only holds if the mean free path of a gas is smaller than the pore size (i.e. if the gas molecules collide with each other within the pore spaces). In a review into experimentation and gas transport in argillaceous geological materials Tomlinson (1988) reported pore radii in various UK clays and claystones. These radii range from 5×10^{-5} m in macropores to 1.6×10^{-9} m in micropores. Shales in the USA have radii of 2.2 to 27.9×10^{-9} m. Coal pore radii, which depend on the composition of the coal, are quoted between 1.5×10^{-10} and 6×10^{-10} m. For methane at atmospheric pressure the mean free path length is about 5×10^{-8} m which is likely to be much smaller than the pore size in a fractured rock and hence in this case Fickian diffusion will occur.

Consideration of diffusion through small pores requires the introduction of the concept of the Knudsen diffusion mechanism that operates when the molecular mean free path is large compared to the pore sizes. Knudsen diffusion becomes important if the pressure is sufficiently low or the pore sizes are sufficiently small that the gas molecules collide mainly with the pore walls and rarely experience collisions with other molecules (Cummingham and Williams, 1980). At atmospheric pressure, diffusional fluxes of methane through air-filled micropores are much smaller than the fluxes predicted from Fick's First Law (Lerman, 1979). An equation for the estimation of Knudsen diffusion coefficients is given in Appendix F.6.3. When the molecular mean free path is of the same general magnitude as the pore sizes of the medium, the diffusion flux includes molecular and Knudsen components. This situation is generally referred to as the transition region. A useful review of the mathematics of diffusion is given in Crank (1979).

While these methods for calculating gas diffusion are valid in deep situations where no pressure differentials exist, they become of limited value in trying to model shallow systems where hydrodynamic flow and gas pressure variations dominate the migration process. There have been few estimates of fluxes of volatiles in typical geosphere environments. In a review, Bath and Falck (1991) reported measurement of biogenic methane fluxes of up to 88 ml/m^2 per day by diffusion out of organic rich coastal marine sediments, and 2.1×10^6 moles of methane per year from Mono Lake in California (Oremland $et\ al.$, 1987).

6.1.2 Viscous flow

Viscous flux is caused by the existence of a pressure gradient with the gas flowing from the high pressure region to the low pressure region. A pressure gradient which will produce a mass movement of gas may develop from the production of gas in a confined space such as after the completion and capping of a landfill or from natural fluctuations in atmospheric pressure or in the elevation of the water table. A temperature gradient will also give rise to pressure differences and lead to gas migration. Generally these pressures and changes in ambient conditions are of little significance in comparison to gaseous diffusion in affecting the transfer of gas between soils and the atmosphere (Baver $et\ al.$, 1972). However, if gaseous exchange between the ground and the atmosphere is restricted by clay or another low permeability medium, large fluxes may be channelled through areas where the seal is breached as a result of atmospheric pressure changes rather than by diffusion.

Viscous fluxes in porous media are generally described by Darcy's Law (see Appendix F.4) which relates viscous volume flux directly to pressure gradient and porous medium permeability, and inversely to gas viscosity.

6.1.3 Gas mixing and layering

A knowledge of the mixing behaviour of gases is essential to an understanding of the problems associated with the entry and subsequent possible accumulation of gases in buildings or other confined spaces (Edwards, 1989).

Mixing of an intrusive gas with the ambient air takes place under the actions of diffusion, turbulent jet mixing, buoyancy or turbulent interaction with ventilating air. Of these processes gas mixing by molecular diffusion is extremely slow. The effect of mixing is to dilute the gas progressively as the gas travels away from the point of leakage.

The factors which influence the build-up of gas concentration as gas is released into an enclosure are gas density, gas source characteristics and ventilation. The density of the gas affects the tendency of the gas to form a layer either in the upper or lower part of the enclosure. The formation of a layer inhibits gas mixing and can influence to a large extent the time taken for an explosive mixture to form. When tunnelling in gassy ground, the possibility of methane layering must be considered when designing the ventilation system. Because methane is buoyant relative to air, layers of methane may form at or near the upper sections of tunnels. These can be difficult to remove if the ventilation velocity is insufficient to disperse the gas entering the air current. Equations which allow the required ventilation velocity to be calculated are given in Appendix F.5. The position of gas ingress into a tunnel is important. A methane leak near the floor will establish a uniform concentration between the point of leakage and the ceiling whereas a leak near the ceiling will result in a shallow ceiling layer of high concentration. The tendency for layering to form in a particular case will depend on the direction of airflow, tunnel gradient and the roughness and composition of the walls.

6.1.4 Dissolved gases

Methane, carbon dioxide etc. may not always exist in the subsurface in the gaseous form, but may be dissolved in groundwater to an extent depending on the pressure, temperature and the concentration of other gases or minerals in the water. Dissolved gases may be carried in and by groundwater, and only when the pressure is reduced and the solubility limit of the gas in water is exceeded, will they bubble out of solution and form a separate gaseous phase. Pressure release will occur whenever a tunnel is excavated or may result from drilling a borehole into the ground. At Abbeystead, groundwater containing methane, normally at a hydrostatic pressure of several hundred metres, entered the tunnel which was at atmospheric pressure (Health and Safety Executive, 1985). The methane came out of solution in the same way that carbon dioxide bubbles out of a lemonade bottle when the top is unscrewed.

6.2 INFLUENCES ON GAS MIGRATION

6.2.1 Meteorological conditions

Gases may exsolve from groundwater and/or be released from the soil as a result of atmospheric pressure changes. It has been found that the rate of change of atmospheric pressure is more important than its absolute value, i.e. rapid changes in air pressure have the greatest effect on the emission rate of the gas (Young, 1991). Although the volumes released per unit area may be small, large fluxes of methane could be generated locally if all the release were channelled through one point such as a fracture or where a clay seal is absent or breached by excavation. Open coal workings such as those worked by pillar and stall methods are often connected to the surface by mineshafts, subsidence cracks, or boreholes.

It is known that changes in atmospheric pressure can cause a sucking or blowing of wells or shafts with the expulsion of mine gases as the underground pressure equilibrates with the new atmospheric pressure. Water table fluctuations occur in response to barometric changes as well as rainfall and these may also affect the interchange of gas between the atmosphere and the ground. Other influences on gas interchange between the ground and the atmosphere include the degree of water saturation of the soil and ground freezing. Frozen ground or the downward permeation of rainwater may result in a significant reduction in porosity and effectively seal the ground surface. This may temporarily block existing migration pathways and allow new pathways (for example lateral rather than vertical pathways) to form. Furthermore, gas accumulation may occur and gas may escape in large concentrations as the temporary seal disintegrates.

Wind, which produces a Venturi effect, and temperature variations which may be diurnal or seasonal, may produce pressure gradients and lead to gaseous interchange between the ground and the atmosphere, but these are probably of lesser importance. Buoyancy effects and temperature effects are much less important to transport than diffusion and pressure changes.

6.2.2 Geological factors

The potential for the movement of gas away from its source will depend on the geological characteristics of the adjoining strata. Natural pathways include consolidated or unconsolidated permeable rock, faults, fractures, fissures, joints and bedding planes. Permeable strata leading from gas reservoirs, coal measures and cavities in limestone provide routes of movement either in the gas phase or in groundwater as dissolved gas. Where methane-containing strata are affected by tidally induced variations in groundwater levels, gas may be pumped out of the strata by a piston effect as the water level rises, or gas emissions may cease as the water level falls.

In varied lithologies, gas will tend to migrate preferentially through beds of rock whose grain size, shape and packing are such as to make them most permeable. Gas may reach the surface some distance from its source by travelling through these strata and could then pass into service ducts or buildings. Gas from landfill sites is known to migrate for hundreds of metres where suitable pathways exist. Ground permeability is rarely consistent over large areas and even very low permeability strata such as clays may contain zones of higher permeability such as sand lenses which may act as migration pathways.

6.2.3 Migration paths in mining areas

Various features of mineworking areas that produce migration pathways or modify the rate of migration were considered by Barry and Raybould (1988) and include:

— the underground workings themselves

— rock fractures associated with the workings

— boreholes

— fluctuating water levels.

Landfilled opencast sites and brick-clay pits frequently coincide with areas previously worked by underground methods in shallow seams. Although such workings usually collapse very shortly after coal extraction, the collapsed material will itself have enough voidage to act as an effective migration path for gas. Thus, if gas can reach such features, then its migration can be as extensive as the mining network. The existence and nature of official underground works are generally well documented but there are also likely to be ancient, unrecorded, unofficial or illegal diggings. Such activities may, however, be indicated in opencast exploration drilling records, or in reports of other site investigations in the area, e.g. for housing. The likelihood of the presence of old workings can also be assessed from the thickness of the seams and quality of the coal in the area.

Rock fractures associated with mineworkings are of various types: natural fractures or other planar openings found in all rock types; joints, which are open but have no displacement and may occur in systematic sets; faults, on which there is displacement of adjacent rock masses but not always an actual opening; and bedding planes between strata in sedimentary rocks (including coal measures). Various geological techniques may be used to predict and map such features and hence identify possible migration routes.

Other fractures relate to blasting and subsidence. Blasting fractures can occur in rocks around the perimeter of a former opencast, or other quarry and may penetrate several metres into surrounding strata. Even where the mineworkings are at a considerable depth, surface or near-surface subsidence can occur. In situations where only one seam has been worked and the position and size of the workings are known, it is possible to predict zones of subsidence fracturing fairly accurately. In practice, however, matters are usually complicated by mining having proceeded at several different depths and in several directions. Thus, an area underlain by a number of workable seams can be assumed to be affected by randomly orientated and distributed fractures, particularly within the more brittle sandstone strata.

Boreholes drilled either for coal exploration or for other purposes, may form conduits for gas if they intersect other forms of migration path. Boreholes should normally be backfilled after drilling (unless lined and retained for monitoring purposes) but this cannot always be relied upon. Thus, since even a single borehole can be critical in some circumstances, an effort should always be made to locate any that may have been drilled in the vicinity of a landfill, before redevelopment begins. Unfortunately, as there is no comprehensive requirement for the registration of boreholes in Britain, this effort can be considerable. The National Geosciences Data Centre at the British Geological Survey holds information on around 600 000 boreholes in the UK and new information is constantly being added.

Gas migration can be influenced very significantly by changing water levels, associated with mine dewatering for example. The cessation of pumping when a mine is abandoned leads to a gradual rise in water levels and this may act as a piston or diaphragm on the mine gas reservoir or the base of a landfill located above The rising water table simply causes an increase in pressure in the gas which may increase gas emission rates or affect the location at which the gas emerges. Former pathways may be cut off and new pathways may be formed (see Figure 18). Some of these new pathways may be related to collapse of the rock fabric or shear failure due to flooding of the adits. Seasonal effects such as hard ground frost and changes in atmospheric pressure or other effects such as groundwater abstraction can significantly change the gas migration pathways and the rate and location of gas emissions (Barry, 1987).

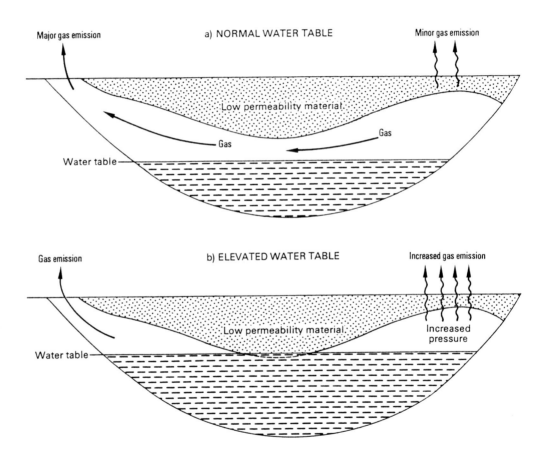

Figure 18 *Effect of change of water table level on gas emissions (after Barry, 1986)*

Staff *et al.,* (1991) discussed the potential for methane migration in longwall mining systems. They highlighted the following points with regard to the potential for methane migration (see Figure 19):

1. The zone Z1 can extend for three to eight times the height of the extracted seam. Zone Z1 is essentially a high permeability structure of broken ground and can be considered isotropic.

2. In zone Z2 the permeability is anisotropic, being greater parallel to the bedding plane than normal to it. The height of Z2 can extend to around 100 m.

3. Above and below the zone Z2 there usually exist in coal measures strata, relaxed strata, zone Z3, where rocks are much less fissured. The relaxation can be sufficient for the strata to become permeable although this is usually parallel to the bedding planes. If leakage paths intersect this zone, such as boreholes, excavations, zones of higher workings and geological faults, then methane can migrate upwards. The strata within these zones themselves may also be sources of methane.

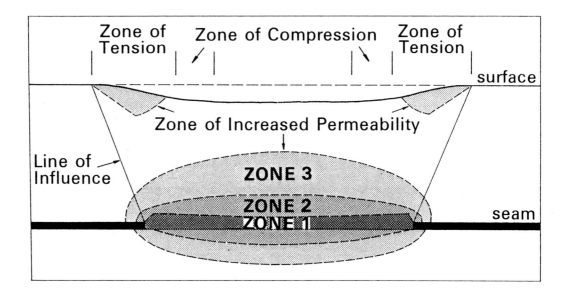

Figure 19 *Permeability zones in longwall mining (after Staff et al., 1991)*

The depth to the top of zone Z2 is considered as critical in the potential for mine gas methane to be emitted at the ground surface. Various factors modify this; thus man-made flow paths (such as boreholes, shafts, old workings), natural flow paths (such as faults or dipping strata) increase the potential for surface emissions for a given depth to zone Z2. The presence of a thick, strong bridging or low permeability upper stratum, or limited extraction techniques (e.g. pillar and stall rather than longwall mining) reduce the potential.

6.2.4 Underground works intersecting groundwaters

Except in major engineering works involving deep tunnelling or shaft sinking, it is unlikely that very high water pressures will be encountered such that methane will be released in significant quantities when the pressure is reduced to atmospheric. However, some site investigation boreholes may reach depths of several tens of metres in certain environments (e.g. in off-shore sediments or in ground with peat layers, where there may be an overpressured aquifer containing gas), and methane could be released. Drilling into a confined aquifer containing dissolved methane, and allowing groundwater to flow from the borehole under artesian pressure, may be a common mode for the release of methane. It is essential that such degassing is not allowed to occur in confined spaces where an explosive mixture could easily develop (see Section 6.5.4).

6.2.5 Other man-made influences

There are many potential gas migration pathways which are man-made. Sewers, the backfill surrounding pipes or cableways, service ducts used for electricity, telephone, TV cables, streetlight cables, water and gas pipes, drains and land drains may all provide pathways and/or voids (such as maintenance chambers) along which gas may migrate and/or accumulate. The underground services which enter buildings provide pathways into underfloor spaces and basements where gas may accumulate (see Figure 20).

Made-up ground, e.g. land covered in tarmac or other relatively impermeable materials like concrete or clay, may influence the migration route of an underlying methane source, forcing the gas to travel laterally to another point or area of emergence.

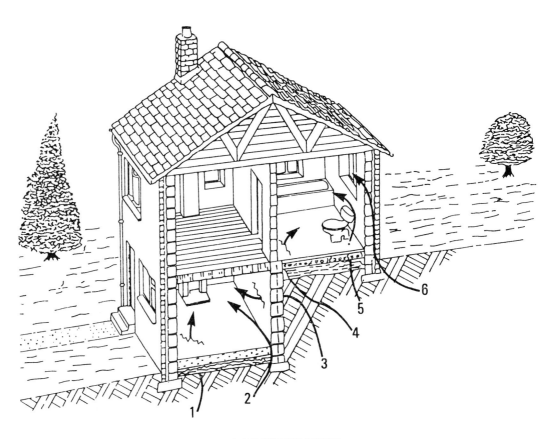

KEY TO INGRESS ROUTES

1. Through cracks in solid floors
2. Through construction joints
3. Through cracks in walls below ground level
4. Through gaps in suspended concrete or timber floor
5. Through gaps around service pipes
6. Through cavities in walls

Figure 20 *Gas ingress routes into a building*

6.3 IDENTIFYING MIGRATION PATHWAYS

The identification of a pathway by which a gas can migrate from the source has to start with the collection of geological and hydrogeological data and their interpretation. Further information, for example, on the position of services such as sewers, cable ducts etc. and about operations such as mining or landfilling (which may have ceased), provides indications as to potential gas sources and/or migration pathways.

In cases where gases are dissolved in groundwater the regional flow of groundwater may have to be assessed, taking into account areas of water recharge and discharge and often the disposition of major tectonic features such as faults which may form primary migration pathways for dissolved gases from depth.

Hydrogeological assessments rely on accurate measurement of piezometric pressure and the sampling and chemical analysis of groundwater obtained during site investigation drilling. If methane is dissolved in groundwater then it is important that adequate sampling systems are available to obtain water samples at their *in-situ* pressure so that the sample does not de-gas as it undergoes de-pressurisation to atmospheric pressure. In general, background knowledge of typical methane concentrations in groundwater is not well defined by the existing data. The organic content and oxidation state of groundwater are important parameters in assessing whether conditions are favourable for methanogenesis to occur. If conditions for methane production exist, the potential for methane migration in or from the groundwater also exists.

During migration, methane can be oxidised aerobically to carbon dioxide and water as a result of bacterial activity. Under anaerobic conditions methane can also be oxidised to carbon dioxide in association with sulphate-reducing bacteria although the exact mechanism for this is not clear. Thus, the presence of carbon dioxide may be indicative of the presence of methane in the general environment. The fact that methane can be oxidised also means that using the ratio of methane to carbon dioxide is not a reliable indicator of a specific methane source (see Sections 5.1 to 5.4).

6.4 GAS MIGRATION MODELLING

As discussed in Section 6.1, gas can migrate from a buried source by two mechanisms, convection because of a pressure gradient or diffusion because of a concentration gradient. Unless diffusion is prevented, for example by the presence of an impermeable surface layer so that pressure build-up occurs, diffusion processes are likely to be dominant. Convection through by-pass routes is likely to be more important in winter when the ground surface is frozen or waterlogged or where natural or man-made seals exist.

Ghabaee and Rodwell (1989) have reviewed the modelling of gas migration, specifically with respect to landfill sites. They concluded that the key transport parameters that should be specified for gas migration modelling are the permeability and porosity of the geological strata surrounding the source or landfill (and of the landfill material where landfills are being studied), the gas viscosity and the binary molecular diffusion coefficients. Water can also be a dominant influence on gas migration. It may obstruct or enhance the gas flow by capillary and gravity effects.

Porosity and permeability

Porosity and permeability are the most elementary measurements of porous media which describe their transmissivity and storage characteristics. Many measurements of permeabilities and porosities of cores of rocks of interest to the oil, gas and water industries can be found in the literature (Elliot *et al.*, 1989; Tomlinson, 1988; Berg, 1986). Many measurements are kept by the National Rivers Authority and the British Geological Survey.

Porosity is defined as the ratio of void space in a rock to the bulk volume of that rock. Porosity may be classified according to its mode of origin as original or induced. Original porosity is developed during the deposition of the sediment material, e.g. the intergranular porosity of sandstones. Induced porosity is that developed by some process subsequent to deposition of the rock, e.g. fractures and faults. Porosity is independent of the grain size of the rock or sediment, but dependent on the mode of packing. Effective porosity is that portion available for water flow, while interconnected porosity is that portion that can be saturated by water.

Permeability is a measure of the capacity of the medium to transmit fluids. Equations for estimating the permeability of a porous medium are given in Appendix F.6.

Gas viscosity

The viscosity of a gas increases with increasing temperature. Equations for the calculation of the temperature dependence of viscosity are given in Appendix F.6.2.

Gas binary diffusion coefficients

For a binary gas mixture the binary gas diffusion coefficient at low pressures is inversely proportional to pressure, increases with increasing temperature and is independent of composition. A comprehensive list of critically reviewed gas binary diffusion coefficients is given in Marrero and Masson (1972).

Binary gas diffusion in a porous medium is also a function of those properties which characterise the porous matrix and the presence of any liquid which partially or fully saturates the porous medium. Pandey *et al.*, (1974) found that capillary pressure, permeability, porosity, resistivity factor and pore size distribution were the prime parameters which defined the diffusion coefficients. Karimi *et al.*, (1988) found that the binary gas diffusion coefficient for a methane-nitrogen mixture was reduced by roughly three orders of magnitude when water was present in the porous medium, and attributed this to the creation of a different pore structure due to the swelling of clays as water was absorbed.

Knudsen diffusion coefficients

Cummingham and Williams (1980) developed a relationship for the determination of Knudsen diffusion coefficients, assuming that Knudsen diffusion (see Section 6.1.1) is dependent on the ratio of the mean molecular free path to the pore radius of the porous medium. This is included in Appendix F.6.3.

Ghabaee and Rodwell (1989) presented mathematical models using the above parameters and a combination of previous models. These included the work by Findikakis and Leckie (1979) on the flow of gas mixtures through landfill sites, the models of Moore (1979) which simulate methane recovery from landfill sites by calculating the diffusive flux of gases through porous media; and the 'dusty gas model' (reviewed in Mason and Malinauskas, 1983; Cummingham and Williams,1980) which describes multicomponent gas transport through porous media and is derived from the kinetic theory of a gas mixture containing very large molecules or dust particles.

They concluded that the basic physics of gas migration in porous media seems to be reasonably well defined, but that gas migration with respect to landfill conditions is not well understood. In particular, they concluded that the relative importance of diffusion and advection in gas migration and in determining the distribution of the gases is unclear; that the effect of water on gas movement has not been well characterised by numerical models or in field studies; that the effect of heterogeneity in the surrounding strata on gas migration is not well understood and that the effect of changes in atmospheric pressure on gas migration has not been modelled.

In a study on the diffusion of light hydrocarbons in shales forming a caprock over a hydrocarbon gas-condensate accumulation Krooss *et al.*, (1988) concluded that considerable diffusive transport of light hydrocarbons had occurred. Their model is summarised in Section 6.5.3. By using an approach of matching geological evidence, analytical data and experimental results to the largest possible extent, they concluded that further research into well defined geological systems with experimental measurements is required to improve the understanding of the diffusive process in nature.

6.5 EXAMPLES AND CALCULATIONS OF SIMPLE GAS SITUATIONS

The following sections present model cases which serve to illustrate situations in which the migration of methane may occur and include calculations to estimate the change of methane concentrations in confined spaces, the rates of diffusion through rocks of varying permeability and how the degradation rate of organic matter may affect the emission rate of methane at the surface.

6.5.1 Methane from buried grass cuttings

The following model case illustrates the potential for methane production and subsequent emission from a ditch filled with grass cuttings. This example is included to illustrate that relatively small volumes of organic matter such as grass cuttings have a considerable potential for methane production.

In plan the ditch has a 2 × 3 m rectangular area; in section it forms a v-shaped trench 1.5 m deep.

Volume of the trench = $0.5 \times 2 \times 1.5 \times 3 = 4.5 \text{ m}^3$.

Assume that half the ditch volume is filled with grass cuttings and that these cuttings are covered with earth. Assume that free water occupies 60% of the cuttings volume.

Volume of grass $= \left(\dfrac{4500}{2}\right) \times 0.4 = 900 \text{ litres}$

If the density of the grass is 0.9 kg/l, the mass of the grass is therefore 810 kg. Of this, 90% is bound water; therefore, the dry weight of the grass is 81 kg. The chemical composition of the grass can be represented as $(C_6H_{10}O_5)_n$ i.e. a linked polymer of glucose units, $C_6H_{12}O_6$, to form cellulose. The proportion by mass which is carbon is given by the atomic weights as

$$\left[n6 \times \frac{12}{n} \, (6 \times 12 + 10 \times 1 + 5 \times 16) \right]$$

The mass of carbon in the dry grass is therefore $81 \times [72/162] = 36$ kg.

If fermentation takes place and generates CH_4 and CO_2 in equal molar proportions, half the 36 kg of carbon will be converted to methane gas (providing the process is 100% efficient).

18 kg of carbon will therefore generate $(18/12) \times 10^3 = 1.5 \times 10^3$ moles of methane.

1 mole of methane occupies 22.4 litres at STP, therefore a maximum total methane yield can be estimated:

maximum total methane yield = $1.5 \times 10^3 \times 22.4 = 3.36 \times 10^4$ litres or 34 m^3.

Depending on the ground conditions, this gas would be produced over a considerable time. For an averaged emission rate of 1 litre/m^2/day over the 6 m^2 area of trench, the source would last for $(3.36 \times 10^4 / 6) = 5600$ days i.e. 15.3 years.

A similar 'worst case' treatment could be applied to the situation of a buried carcase, for example, with the difference that the total carbon mass would be estimated from another formula neglecting the non-degradable carbon present in the skeletal bones.

The above example is a hypothetical calculation to illustrate the worst possible case, and the following points should be noted:

1. The conversion of carbon in the grass to methane and carbon dioxide is unlikely to be 100% efficient.

2. It is possible that a proportion of the methane might be oxidised to carbon dioxide, depending on the ground conditions.

3. The model does not take into account changes in the ecosystem and meteorological conditions. Precipitation rates might increase or decrease the emission of methane depending on the overall conditions and freezing of the ground (and the grass) would temporarily prevent the production and emission of methane.

6.5.2 Methane diffusion rates through sandstone

The rate of diffusion of a gas through a permeable medium can be estimated if its diffusion coefficient in free air is known by using Millington's Law (see Equation F.2 in Appendix F.2):

$$\frac{D}{D_o} = \phi^{1.33}$$

where D is the effective diffusion coefficient in the porous medium, D_o is the diffusion coefficient in air, and ϕ is the porosity of the medium.

For methane the diffusion coefficient in free air (D_o) is approximately 1.5×10^{-5} m²/s and therefore the effective diffusion coefficient (D) for a permeable medium of porosity of around 30 % is given by:

$$D = 0.202 \times 1.5 \times 10^{-5} = 3 \times 10{-6} \text{ m}^2/\text{s}.$$

In their study of the gas explosion at Loscoe, Williams and Aitkenhead (1991) used the one-dimensional form of Fick's Second Law to calculate the time it would take for gas to migrate 100 m from a landfill through unsaturated, fractured sandstone and to build up to a concentration of 5% in a confined space (i.e. 100 % LEL), assuming the only migration mechanism was that of diffusion.

The one-dimensional form of Fick's Law and its solution are given in Appendix F.3 (Equations F.4 and F.5 respectively). The solution is restated here for clarity:

$$\frac{C}{C_0} = erfc \left\{ \frac{x}{2(Dt)^{0.5}} \right\}$$

where t is the time in seconds for the final methane concentration, C, to reach 5 volume % at a distance, x, from the point of initial methane concentration, $C_0 = 60$ volume %.

The diffusion coefficient of methane in the sandstone, D, is 3×10^{-6} m²/s.

Therefore, $\dfrac{C}{C_0} = erfc\{z\} = \dfrac{5}{60} = 0.083$

Tables for $erfc\{z\} = 0.083$ give $z = 1.23$.

Therefore, $t = \dfrac{x^2}{(4D.1.51)} = \dfrac{x^2}{6.05D}$

For a house 100 m from the landfill edge, the time taken for methane to diffuse and attain a concentration of 5 volume % will be:

$$t = \frac{100^2}{6.05 \times 3 \times 10^{-6}} \text{ seconds or 17.5 years}$$

In contrast, if diffusion were to take place in free air e.g. through open mine workings or large fractures in sandstone, limestone etc., the time to reach 5% methane concentration would be:

$$\frac{100^2}{\left(6.05 \times 1.5 \times 10^{-5}\right)} = 1.1 \times 10^8 \text{ s or 3.5 years}$$

6.5.3 Diffusion of methane through a caprock

This model is included to allow the comparison between the diffusion time for methane in a porous, unsaturated sandstone (as calculated in the previous model) with diffusion rates in rocks which are typical of caprocks such as low porosity sandstones or shale. The model was presented by Krooss *et al.*, (1988) in a study of the concentrations of light hydrocarbons in shales forming a caprock over a hydrocarbon gas-condensate accumulation. It uses the one-dimensional form of Fick's Law (as in the previous model) to estimate the diffusion of light hydrocarbons into a thick homogeneous caprock.

The caprock was assumed to have an initial hydrocarbon (e.g. methane) concentration of C_0. The concentration of the hydrocarbon within the caprock at the boundary with the reservoir was denoted C_1.

A diffusion front was (arbitrarily) defined as the location within the caprock where the concentration of the hydrocarbon is one half the difference with the concentration at the contact, i.e. where the concentration is 0.5 $(C_1 - C_0)$.

The authors produced a schematic model to show the advance of the diffusion front (as defined above) of the hydrocarbon with time (see Figure 21). The concentration profiles in this diagram show how the diffusion front will advance into the medium with time. The rate of advance of the front depends on the diffusion coefficient, D, which is a function of the properties of the medium, the diffusing species, temperature and pressure.

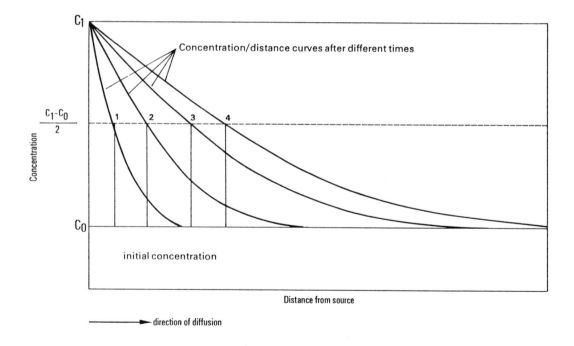

Figure 21 *Mathematical diffusion model – diffusion front defined by 1/2 ($C_1 - C_0$) (after Krooss et al., 1988)*

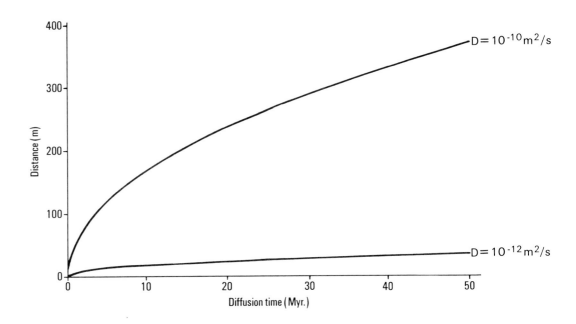

Figure 22 *Diffusion distances with geological time – advance of the 1/2 ($C_1 - C_0$) concentration front, from a constant source C_1 (after Krooss et al., 1988)*

Based on measured or estimated diffusion coefficients for light hydrocarbons in sedimentary rocks, Krooss *et al.* (1988) calculated the distance a diffusion front can advance in a caprock in geological time (see Figure 22). The diffusion coefficient values applied to the model were between limits of 10^{-10} m²/s for sandstone and 10^{-12} m²/s for shale. Using these values they calculated that a concentration difference corresponding to one half the concentration difference at the source may be reached at a distance of about 400 m from the source within 50 million years for the sandstone, whereas for the shale this concentration difference is only achieved at a distance of less than 40 m from the source for the same time.

6.5.4 Methane release rates during groundwater pumping

Figure 23 is a schematic representation of a confined aquifer which contains water saturated with dissolved methane at a partial pressure equivalent to the *in-situ* hydrostatic pressure. Water is discharged from the aquifer by pumping at the surface, and the pressure difference between water at the surface (at atmospheric pressure) and water in the aquifer is represented by the height of the head of water, H.

The amount of methane released by each litre of water as it reaches the surface and is depressured can be calculated by using a modified form of Henry's Law. Here the mass of methane dissolved in groundwater at 10°C is given by $m = 29.9 \times P$, where m is in mg of dissolved methane per litre of water and P is the partial pressure of the gas in atmospheres (see Appendix A.2). If the pressure difference is H atmospheres, the mass of methane released will be $29.9 \times H$ mg per litre of water. If the aquifer is saturated to a partial pressure of methane of 3 atmospheres then H has a value of 2 atmospheres, and the amount of methane gas released per litre of pumped water would be about 60 mg, equivalent to 84 ml STP.

To fill an unventilated chamber of volume 125 m³ to a 100% LEL level requires an accumulation of 6250 litres of methane gas. The number of litres of pumped water needed to give 6250 litres of methane is:

$$\frac{6250}{0.084} = 74\,405 \text{ (or } 74.4 \text{ m}^3)$$

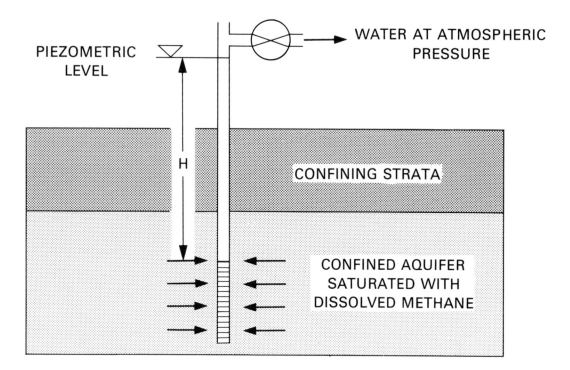

PRESSURE REDUCTION OF H BETWEEN
AQUIFER AND DISCHARGE WATER

Figure 23 *Pressure release during pumping*

If the pump rate were 5000 m³ per day, an explosive mixture would form in an unventilated chamber in only 21 minutes.

It is worth noting that if the pumped water is allowed to equilibrate with the air once it is at the surface, then most of the 29.9 mg of methane remaining in the water would de-gas. As noted in Sections 2.1.1 and 3.1.2, methane has a very low solubility in water which is in equilibrium saturation with air at one atmosphere. This is because the partial pressure of methane in air is very low (1.6×10^{-6} atmosphere; see Table 5). The concentration of dissolved methane would drop from 29.9 mg per litre to a negligible value given by:

$$m = 29.9 \times 1.6 \times 10^{-6} = 4.78 \times 10^{-5} \text{ mg per litre of water.}$$

Air equilibration of the water in the chamber would therefore increase the rate at which the 100% LEL level would be attained.

6.5.5 Methane accumulation in a confined space

This simple example considers the consequence of a methane-containing gas issuing into a confined space from four boreholes:

− gas contains 50% methane

− gas emission rate is 1 litre/hour per borehole into an unventilated space

− size of unventilated space (or room) is 2.5 (height) × 2 × 2 m; volume is 10 m³

− duration of gas emission is 100 uninterrupted hours.

Volume of gas entering room in 100 hours	= 4 x 1 x 100	= 400 litres
Volume of methane entering room in 100 hours	= 0.5 x 400	= 200 litres
Concentration of methane in room after 100 hours	= 200/(10 x 1000) x 100	= 2 %.

Therefore, the time to reach 5 volume % (100% LEL) would be 250 hours.

6.5.6 Tunnel ventilation velocities

In this example the minimum ventilation velocity to prevent methane layering in a tunnel is calculated. Equations to calculate ventilation velocities are given in Appendix F.5. For methane in air:

$$U = \left(\frac{L}{1.63}\right)\left[\frac{q}{W}\right]^{\frac{1}{3}}$$

where
U = the ventilation velocity (m/s)
L = the Layering Number (dimensionless)
q = the rate of ingress of the gas (m³/s)
W = the width of the layer (m).

In the case of a horizontal tunnel it is necessary to keep the Layering Number greater than 5. In a tunnel 2 m wide with methane entering at a rate of 0.1 m³/s the minimum ventilation velocity will be given by:

$$U = \left(\frac{5}{1.63}\right) \times \left[\frac{0.1}{2}\right]^{\frac{1}{3}} = 1.13 \text{ m/s}$$

Therefore, in order to prevent the formation of a methane layer the ventilation velocity must be greater than 1.13 m/s.

7 Construction situations and methane hazards

In regions where coal mines have been closed, existing buildings and engineered structures may not be immune from the threat of underground seepages of methane from unventilated workings. Old seams and permeable strata can also provide migration routes for methane from non-coal sources, e.g. landfill gas derived from waste disposal in pits and cavities left by the mining and quarrying activities. New constructions in such areas of disused coal mines and waste-filled quarries and pits require an assessment of risk from methane in the context of possible geological pathways.

Tunnel operations are prone to methane gas problems, sometimes where groundwater seepage or transport are accompanied by de-gassing of dissolved methane or carbon dioxide. Examples are illustrated by the Wyresdale Tunnel/Abbeystead explosion and the ingress of deep-seated gas when tunnelling for the Carsington aqueduct. Tunnelling in gassy ground requires precautions of monitoring in the excavated tunnel and probing in advance of the tunnel workings, for example, as was done during the construction of the Western Interceptor Sewer of the Tyneside Sewerage Scheme. Special designs may be required for sewers and manholes in coal measures strata and gassy ground generally.

With the pressure to develop contaminated land, old landfill sites and dockland areas, many construction situations face the problems of methane. In some cases, such as the Surrey docks development in London, new buildings may require specific designs to prevent the ingress of gases from the ground through underground service ducts and drains into underfloor cavities.

Methane can arise in a number of ways in a site being considered for building development. Apart from coal-mine gas, buried organic-rich materials in nearby localities, such as peat, landfills, covered ponds, lakes and old farmyards etc., may be sources of methane. If a pathway is possible, perhaps involving lateral movement under a seal of concrete or tarmac in made-up ground, then a problem may arise. Sites with underground cavities, concealed shafts, boreholes or tunnels are at risk if methane can fill them and provide a reservoir for leakage into buildings. Identification of such possibilities in the pre-construction site survey are necessary to prevent a problem; curing the problem at a post-construction phase is usually costly. Some case histories are described to illustrate gas problems, uncertainties and points of consideration. As it is difficult to quantify scales, gas volumes, emission rates and risks in a particular situation, *expert advice should be sought when a gas problem has been identified.*

7.1 GENERAL SITUATIONS OF POTENTIAL HAZARDS

There are essentially four types of methane likely to affect construction; deep-seated natural gas, coal mine gas, landfill gas and gas from shallow sources. Whatever the type, the effects of the methane, including associated gases and oxidation products like carbon dioxide, on the physical and chemical integrities of the building materials will have to be assessed. Existing buildings may become at risk from methane because of a change in the practice of local mining or the establishment of a nearby landfill or because of the effects of the construction of another adjacent structure like a tunnel or dam which perturb the underground water and gas regimes. The planning and design of new developments require an understanding of the previous land-use; shallow sources of organic matter and associated methane gas should be investigated as well as the general impacts from the local geology, hydrogeology and local mining and landfill practices. Apart from methane from the coal-bearing rocks themselves, waste disposal sites are very common in coal-bearing strata and these produce bacteriogenic methane. Where coal and other mining areas are being considered for redevelopment, concern about any inherent gas reservoirs at depth should be extended to any shallow landfill sources in the vicinity of the development. Landfill gas as well as the mine gas can migrate through fissures, fractured strata, seams and shafts (Barry and Raybould, 1988).

Building developments on or in the vicinity of contaminated land and made-up ground require site investigation to check for possible shallow methane sources and pathways from landfills and mines. So-called 'inert' materials, such as waste foundry sand fills may be present and acting as a potential source of bacteriogenic methane. Developments in old docklands and in off-shore operations involving river, tidal and marine muds, silts and sediments require an assessment of possible methane risks. The use of building materials which can suffer biodegradable changes *in situ* leading to the production of methane or other gases should be assessed in the post-construction context. Finished works which contain basements or undercrofts may be at risk from methane; ingress of gas into buildings may occur *via* underground service ducts, drains and cables.

7.1.1 Methane from coal mines

The management of the risks from gas involved in coal mining and mining ores are well established and the regulations are clear for establishing adequate ventilation. In the U.K., the legislation (The Health and Safety at Work etc. Act 1974, The Mines and Quarries Acts 1954 – 1971, Orders and Regulations made under those Acts) prescribes the maximum permitted methane (or firedamp) levels:

– 1.25% (25% LEL) methane within general body of mine roadways – shut off electrical power, cease shotfiring etc.

– 2% methane within general body of mine roadways – withdraw workforce.

A combination of ventilation and methane drainage techniques are required to control the levels of methane in gassy mines and to vent the methane harmlessly to the atmosphere. Coal-related methane emissions in Britain are described by Creedy (1991a); British Coal has made progress in promoting mine-gas utilisation schemes by exploiting methane for power and heating purposes.

However, many collieries have exhausted their reserves or are no longer economical to operate. Disused mines constitute large imperfectly sealed gas reservoirs. Part of the procedure for mine closures nowadays is to account for the methane hazards which may appear in the surface environment. Protective measures to control gas leakage include linking old mines to continuing mine ventilation systems, passive venting, controlled flooding and water sealing (Creedy, 1991b). The problems of gas leakages from old unrecorded mine workings have to be treated on an *ad hoc* basis.

Mining-induced fractures, fissures and ground movement arising from workings in an idealised longwall mining system cause widely spread permeability changes in the surrounding rocks; a critical depth for potential surface emission can be defined as typically 100 m, but this is subject to wide variation from many other factors (Staff *et al.,* 1991; see Section 6.2.3). On cessation of pumping, the resultant rise in water level can drive methane from upper workings into permeable horizons above and to the surface *via* faults and fissures. Existing properties might thus be placed at risk; structural precautions become necessary for new residential housing; and 'high risk' areas might not be developed.

7.1.2 Methane in tunnelling and underground works

In general, problems with gases may arise in any of the driving, lining and operational phases of tunnelling. Driving and excavation create disturbed zones of weakness in the surrounding host rock which provide permeable pathways along which gases may travel when differential pressures exist, and along which methane-bearing groundwaters may infiltrate. Where pipelines are being installed by pipe-jacking techniques, annulus voids are created around the pipes forming routes for gas and water. The tunnel, therefore, changes the groundwater flow regime. The nature and cost of the lining may be dictated by the need to prevent the ingress of methane or methane-bearing waters.

According to Pearson (1991), two major underground civil engineering projects encountered methane hazards in the 1980s; these were at Abbeystead in Lancashire and at Carsington in

Derbyshire. Both projects included the construction of long concrete-lined tunnels excavated in sandstone/siltstone/mudstone sequences in Carboniferous strata at depths down to 100 m. The mudstones and shales in these areas are carbonaceous and potential methane sources. Throughout the construction phases neither project suffered major delay through the presence of methane, and in each case, gas in hazardous quantities was only detected after the main tunnelling operations. At Abbeystead, the gas entered a valve house on the Lune-Wyre water transfer system in sufficient quantity to cause an explosive atmosphere (HSE, 1985). At Carsington, although the gas was monitored and detected in small concentrations during excavation, it was only during testing works that methane was measured in potentially hazardous amounts in the C-D tunnel (Pearson and Edwards, 1989). The Carsington aqueduct case is described in more detail elsewhere (Pearson and Edwards, 1989; Pearson and Brown, 1990; Pearson, 1991). Biofilm formation had been observed by Pearson and Brown (1990) in the Carsington aqueduct tunnel where methane-bearing water seepages had occurred. Bacteria using methane for growth may cause local depletion of oxygen, enrichment of carbon dioxide and slippery conditions for workers. The Abbeystead case description is given in Section 7.3.

During the construction of the Western Interceptor Sewer of the Tyneside Sewerage System, the contractor for the Northumbrian Water Authority had to contend with driving tunnels and sinking shafts/manholes in suspected gassy rock of coal measures strata containing old workings. Precautionary practices of forward probing for methane and cavities and monitoring for methane in the tunnel were adopted. Advance probing was carried out by sinking 75 mm drillholes from ground level at 3 m intervals along the proposed centre of tunnel line and making gas measurements with a methanometer.

With reference to tunnelled water schemes, Beresford (1989) made some tentative recommendations for the design of new works. Design, backed up where necessary by operating procedures, should seek to reduce the number of closed voids in which gas could accumulate. Even when a system is kept full of water, the concentration of dissolved methane may increase, for instance in tunnel contents by a process of circulation. Methane in solution enters over lengths where the groundwater pressure exceeds the internal pressure while fresh water is lost over lengths where the groundwater pressure is lower. System contents should be kept safe by regular flushing even when water transfer is not required. Tunnel linings should be made as water-tight as practicable. These measures will help to reduce the scale of the problem as well as reducing water loss and the gain of other harmful substances.

7.1.3 Shafts, wells and dams

Making shafts, wells and boreholes, i.e. vertical open structures in the ground, can create collection points for different gases arriving by diffusion or other means, including transport by water flow. The gas precautions necessary for the entry into sewage wells illustrate the dangers. The use of caissons and cofferdams, the excavation of trenches, pits, cuttings etc. also create hollows into which gases may migrate.

The entry of workers into a shaft well, part of the earth dam structure at the Carsington reservoir, Derbyshire, resulted in a loss of life through asphyxiation by carbon dioxide. Drainage blankets of limestone had been incorporated into an earthfill embankment composed of compacted mudstone. Microbially aided oxidation of the sulphide minerals in the mudrock produced sulphuric acid which reacted with the limestone to produce carbon dioxide. Volume loss from acid leaching may also explain the partial collapse of such a structure (Pye and Miller, 1990).

Building a reservoir by damming a stream or river creates a lake with possible ponding and stagnation of its organic matter which may provide a source of methane in the water. If methane-bearing waters were to leak into the dam structure or associated tunnels, methane accumulations might develop, or, if the methane undergoes oxidation during migration, carbon dioxide might be produced in sufficient quantities to become the hazard.

7.2 CASE HISTORIES

There are very few published case histories and those that are available have few details, e.g. some case histories for a number of different sites can be found in Baker (1989); Barry and Raybould (1988); and Jaitly (1977). The accounts of incidents and accidents can be very useful in focusing attention on the different sources of methane and the different ways in which the gas can migrate or be transported into buildings and tunnels. The case histories of the Abbeystead and Loscoe incidents demonstrate many of the properties of methane and the principles governing its behaviour, described earlier in this report. The lessons for planners, designers, engineers and operators are:

- the need to identify potential regional and local sources of methane

- the need to identify potential pathways

- the need to appreciate the wider impacts of construction works on the environment and with time

- the need to interpret with care evidence which might indicate a methane problem

- the need for flexibility to carry out additional investigations

- the need to attend to design detailing

- the need for caution at all times in underground works in recognition that unpredictable gas releases could occur.

In order to highlight the uncertainties involved with methane problems in construction and the matters which should be considered, some illustrative examples are given in Section 7.5.

7.3 ABBEYSTEAD

7.3.1 Background and location

The Wyresdale Tunnel, about 6.6km long and 2.6 m diameter, is situated in the Bowland Fells, Lancashire, and was constructed in the 1970s as part of a North West Water Authority (NWWA) water management scheme for the transfer of water from the River Lune to the River Wyre. It was the location of a fatal explosion due to ignition of methane gas at the up-gradient Abbeystead valve chamber (NGR SD555540) on 23 May 1984 (Health & Safety Executive, 1985). Seepages of groundwater which were found to be associated with the methane ingress were sampled and analysed by NWWA and BGS shortly after the explosion. Following the earlier mapping of the tunnel section during construction, detailed geological mapping of the area was carried out for NWWA by BGS (BGS, 1985; Johnson, 1981). Subsequent investigations of the methane ingress were carried out for NWWA by Exploration Consultants Ltd. (ECL, 1986). ECL specified and supervised a seismic survey and an assessment of hydrocarbon source rock potential in samples from relevant formations. ECL reported methane ingress data to Sir William Halcrow and Partners with a preliminary interpretation which was refined, as a result of further studies and analysis, for inclusion in their report and recommendations to NWWA (ECL, 1988; Halcrow, 1989). Regular gas phase and water monitoring with analyses by NWWA was carried out from early 1985 to late 1987, yielding a substantial database for methane ingress to the tunnel and meteorological and operational parameters. Further assessment of the continuing methane problem was possible when the tunnel was drained down in late 1987; samples of the methane-containing groundwater seepages were collected for analysis by NWWA and BGS (BGS, 1988). The distribution of water inflows along the tunnel was investigated by dilution of a lithium chloride tracer added to the drainage flow. A fuller account of the work carried out by NWWA and their consultants to investigate the problem and to identify design and operational modifications to alleviate the problem is now available (Orr *et al.*, 1991).

7.3.2 Geology and Hydrogeology

The tunnel is constructed through a Carboniferous sequence of silty mudstones, siltstones and sandstones (Roeburndale Formation) of Namurian age (Millstone Grit Group) which has been folded in a broad anticline and is cut by several faults (Johnson, 1981). The Grizedale Anticline is one of a series with a NE-SW axial trend, superimposed on which are NE-SW trending faults with both normal and reverse displacements. Gravity data for the region suggest a model comprising tilted blocks and half-graben structures. Underlying the Roeburndale Formation (>400 m thickness) is the Bowland Grit Group (>400 m thick) which has more frequent sandy facies, underlain by the Dinantian shale, limestone and sandstone strata of the Carboniferous Limestone. Seismic data confirm the anticlinal structure at both shallow and deep levels in the Namurian-Dinantian sequence with 'structural closure' potentially capable of trapping hydrocarbons; structures in the Dinantian are offset from those in the overlying Namurian (ECL, 1986; Lawrence et al., 1987). The seismic interpretation also suggests that faults might intersect potential porous reservoir formations at depth (ECL, 1986; Lawrence et al., 1987); faulting and shear zones were observed in the tunnel section (Johnson, 1981). The report by ECL concludes that there are high probabilities of potential organic-rich source rocks and reservoir formations through this Namurian-Dinatian sequence (Lawrence et al., 1987). However, no direct confirmation of reservoir rocks and structures was possible in the absence of an exploratory borehole, and studies of porosity in archived Namurian-Dinantian samples from the nearby Whitmoor borehole indicate that their reservoir quality is generally low owing to shales or to cementation. Nevertheless the ECL report concludes that the most probable chance of significant porosity lies in there being localised development of secondary porosity by dissolution of Dinantian carbonate at >1000 m depth or by fracturing. In spite of such hypotheses, the source and reservoir formations for the methane which invades the tunnel are still not known with an acceptable degree of certainty. The geophysical data point to a source-migration-entrapment hypothesis which cannot be evaluated further without exploratory drilling (see Figure 24).

There is a paucity of data on the hydrogeology of this region. The Carboniferous strata have not been developed for large-scale groundwater abstraction, because of their generally poor and unpredictable water-bearing characteristics and the abundance of surface water for public supply (hence the construction of the water transfer tunnel). However, there are a number of shallow wells for domestic supply in the vicinity, mostly taking water from localised horizons in the Millstone Grit below the cover of glacial drift clay. Owing to the variable topography in the area and the isolation of individual water-bearing horizons, groundwater heads may differ quite substantially in different strata and in different wells. The abundant springs in the area represent natural discharges of various groundwater horizons, usually at topographic breaks of slope. A brief review of the hydrogeological data from boreholes, wells and springs in the Abbeystead area was included with a report of hydrochemical data for a small number of these groundwaters (BGS, 1985). The report concluded that because of the paucity of piezometric data, little is known about the scales of groundwater movements and particularly about the interaction between shallow and deep groundwaters in the Carboniferous rocks. The earlier BGS study of methane ingress to the tunnel had identified anomalous chemistry for the methane-bearing groundwater which suggests a distinct, possibly deeper, groundwater which flowed along with the methane via permeable fracturing (BGS, 1984). Groundwater enters the tunnel along the greater part of its length, but predominantly in the vicinity of the Abbeystead (Southern) limb of the anticline penetrated by the tunnel. The rate of entry is generally about 0.8 l/s (0.7 million litres per day), the flow increasing by about 25% when the tunnel is dewatered. Only a small proportion of the inflow was found to have an appreciable content of dissolved methane (Orr et al., 1991). The subsequent hydrochemistry survey found no evidence for leakage elsewhere of this anomalous groundwater into the shallow regime, reinforcing the conclusion that migration is strongly fault-controlled. The initiation of flow of groundwater from deeper into shallower strata requires an upward groundwater gradient. Once initiated, if water at depth contains methane in solution at a concentration in equilibrium with gaseous methane, a 'gas-lift-pump' mechanism is likely to supervene with an appreciable increase in rate of upward transfer of water and methane (Orr et al., 1991). At the pressure and temperature conditions at the depth of the putative deep reservoir, methane solubility will be about 1500 mg per litre, compared with the figure of about 28 mg/l at surface conditions of one atmosphere partial pressure of methane. Therefore, substantial amounts of methane can be transported in solution at depth.

Location of water ingress		NO			
Range of methane concentration	mg/l	SIGNIFICANT	12-27	<1-12	<1-17
Approximate cumulative water inflow	l/s	INGRESS	<1	1	4

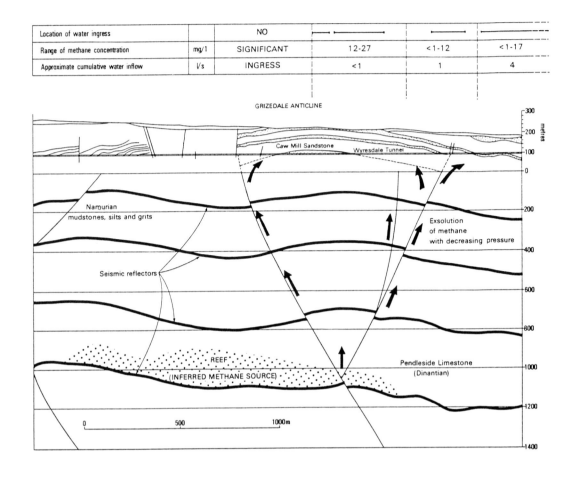

Figure 24 *Geological section at the Wyresdale tunnel with simplified seismic data and gas and water ingress locations (after Orr et al., 1991)*

7.3.3 Gas fluxes and migration

The monitoring carried out by NWWA showed only slight long-term fluctuations in gas ingress to the water-filled tunnel. On account of the extent of storage of methane in water contained in the tunnel, no comprehensive analysis could be made of the causes of the variations of the measured rate of ingress of methane (in water and air) at Abbeystead. Rates of pumping and barometric pressure were significant, particularly when combined as total pressure, but data do not allow effects of rainfall intensity to be assessed (Orr *et al.,* 1991). A mean value of about 8 kg/day of methane enters the water-filled tunnel; in this condition, about 50 % of the methane enters as free gas, the rest in groundwater solution. Three days after the tunnel dewatering in late 1987, the methane ingress was estimated to be about 140 kg/day, although this rate declined approximately exponentially (with allowance for atmospheric pressure) with time. This decay in methane ingress supports the hypothesis of a low pressure upper trap at the tunnel level, fed by gas migration from the deep reservoir (Orr *et al.,* 1991). The bulk of the gas enters over a short length of lined tunnel corresponding to the intersection with the faulted sandstone units in the core and limb of the Grizedale Anticline. ECL suggest that the flux is derived from a Dinantian limestone reservoir at about 1100 m depth (11 MPa pressure) with an 85% probability of containing 7×10^6 m^3 of recoverable gas at 40°C; ECL assumed a leakage of 20 m^3/day (14.3 kg/day) and thus a lifetime of over 900 years which gives an idea of the potential longevity of such natural seepages. It is not clear what artificial measures, short of drilling into and draining the reservoir, could be taken to control or confine the seepage except in relatively small near-surface zones. The ECL report speculates that fault-controlled migration of gas will be sensitive to compressive stress and therefore to neotectonics in the region. Thus a stress field oriented such that fractures will be kept open by a shearing effect will favour gas migration; it is suggested that the stresses induced by neotectonics in the Abbeystead region may have contributed to enhancing fault permeabilities either transiently or semi-permanently. Migration of gaseous species through the fault system requires that an excess pressure be built up, although this is predicted to be minimised in a system of open fractures. 'Channelling' within the faults, along irregularities in rock surfaces and intersections between fractures, is likely to concentrate pathways. The possibility of fracture networks in the vicinity of the tunnel having been reactivated due to stress changes induced by construction itself also has to be considered.

7.3.4 Gas source

There is considerable uncertainty about the depth and nature of the methane source rock and trapping formation, as described above. The methane is attributed to a geological source on the basis of evidence on how it enters the tunnel, the net fluxes and continuity of flux, and so on. Alternative sources which had to be considered and were subsequently rejected were organic detritus accumulating as sludge in the tunnel itself, and other remote sources of biogenic methane such as animal wastes from farms and waste disposal sites in the vicinity (of which there are none). Analytical data for the associated gases and isotopic composition of methane provide evidence for its source and subsequent processes occurring during migration. The analyses of gases dissolved in tunnel seepage waters in November 1987 showed that the ethane/methane ratio is very low, $<0.02\%$ (BGS, 1988). Analyses during an intensive monitoring phase in 1985 showed rather more substantial proportions of ethane, up to 0.3% (ECL, 1986), and also suggested that the ethane concentration increased significantly when tunnel pumping ceased. This observation and the apparent analytical discrepancies remain unexplained. Predominance of methane over its homologue alkane hydrocarbon ethane is usually thought to be diagnostic of either a biological source of methane or a thermogenic origin as 'dry gas' produced by thermal cracking of source organics under deeper, hotter geological conditions than those corresponding to the 'oil window' and 'wet gases' (see Sections 3.2.3 and 4.2).

The stable $^{13}C/^{12}C$ and $^{2}H/^{1}H$ ratios (represented as $\delta^{13}C$ and $\delta^{2}H$) in the methane were measured by BGS in 1984 and 1987; samples and analytical quality were better in 1987 and those analyses are preferred. The $\delta^{13}C$ and $\delta^{2}H$ values fall in the compositional field of biogenic methane according to the classification by Schoell (1980, 1983) (see Figure 25). It was suggested that the isotopic composition of methane might have undergone physical or chemical alteration during migration into the shallow subsurface thereby reducing the validity of comparison with conventional bulk gas reservoir classifications (BGS, 1988). A similar concept of secondary bacterial modification of the migrating methane and thus of its isotopic composition towards lighter values was also suggested in an ECL report (Halcrow, 1989). Other mechanisms for modifying $\delta^{13}C$ during migration, or for deriving light ^{13}C methane from petroleum cracking, were mentioned in the earlier ECL report (ECL, 1986). Overall, the stable isotope data are not definitive concerning the methane source at Abbeystead, despite such data usually being powerful in distinguishing bulk natural gas field origins.

Other gases, including inert gases, dissolved in the tunnel seeps were also analysed by BGS in 1987. In particular, the dissolved concentrations of methane and helium were strongly correlated. Helium is an inert gas which accumulates over time in groundwaters and in hydrocarbon reservoirs because it is the by-product of radioactive decay of naturally-occurring uranium and thorium (see Section 3.1.2). It is the lightest inert gas (molecular weight 4), and is even more mobile than methane (molecular weight 16). Thus enhanced helium indicates a deeper source for the seepage water than the chemically dissimilar shallow groundwaters, and the correlation implies the same for the methane.

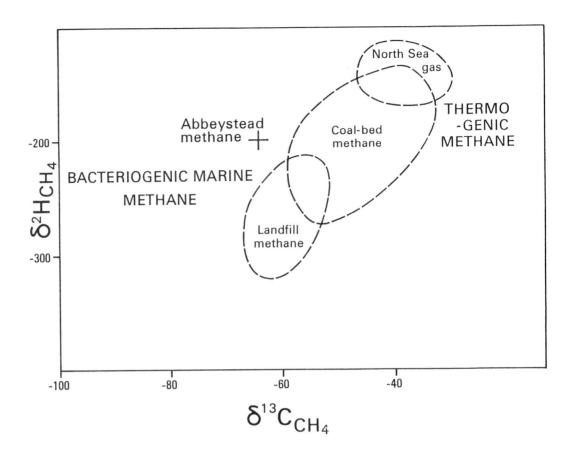

Figure 25 $^{13}C / ^{12}C$ and $^{2}H / ^{1}H$ for methane sources in UK

In summary, there is no unequivocal geological or geochemical proof of a definite source of methane, but the balance of data and interpretation suggests a relatively deep geological source. The gas might have been modified physically, chemically and microbially during its migration as a minor component in the deep groundwater system, and probably accumulated in a shallow trap close to the tunnel.

7.3.5 Lessons on gas hazard detection and investigation

The extensive, but still inconclusive, investigations after the Abbeystead disaster provoke an assessment to be made of methods for predicting geological gas hazard in such constructions. In view of the modes of travel of methane, by diffusion and advection in gaseous form or in solution, a strategy needs to be developed appropriate for the circumstances.

Other recent tunnels have experienced ingress of methane from a deep source at rates comparable to that at Abbeystead (e.g. Carsington − see Section 7.1.2). A well-ventilated tunnel will, during construction, maintain the concentration well below the threshold of detection by the types of portable methanometer normally used. In consequence, unless precise analysis of gas and water samples has been undertaken, it is not possible to state for a particular tunnel that methane was not encountered. As a first step, a gas risk assessment should be carried out by a geological reconnaissance using published maps and information from BGS (in the UK) and other sources, supplemented by further ground surveying if necessary.

In the Abbeystead case, the log of a borehole at Whitmoor about 7 km away from the route of the tunnel was held in BGS files as commercially confidential information. This recorded the presence of non-commercial traces of gas, but was not reported since the enquiry to BGS concerned only geological and hydrogeological information, and gas as a hazard was not widely recognised at that time. Confidentiality of specific data itself is not a barrier to their use in identifying the susceptibility to hazard and the need for precautionary measures, and BGS has well established procedures for making such information available for specific purposes whilst preserving the detail and confidentiality of the data source.

The source of methane may be at depth and in unexplored terrain; and it would be unreasonable to precede every tunnelling project with a site investigation comparable to that undertaken at Abbeystead (after the explosion), revealing — but only *post facto* when an explanation needed to be found to a known phenomenon — a possible deep reservoir.

Unless particular sources and migration modes can be predicted, the design of a suitable form of site investigation to evaluate risk is impracticable, e.g. Orange-Fish Tunnel (Muir Wood, 1975). It may be possible only to establish prior to commitment to a project, the probability of encountering methane at rates of ingress of say 10, 100 or 1000 kg per day. In a high probability of a high rate, the full set of precautions against methane will be taken from the outset. Otherwise, the engineer may elect to adopt the observational approach, whereby a systematic series of observations will be made to test the hypothesis of methane presence, adopting methods of working which will ensure safety from a dangerous concentration until the risk is shown not to exist. Such an approach must consider the possible forms of methane ingress in order to ensure that the most critical combination of circumstances is being addressed (Orr *et al.*, 1991).

If hydrocarbon source evaluation, comprising analyses of identified possible source rocks for organic content and maturity, forms part of the investigation, it should be recognized that it is unlikely to be comprehensive or definitive. There are probably several UK sedimentary strata which have source potential similar to the Abbeystead area rocks. The parallel factor determining hazard — that of structural or sedimentological reservoir control — can only be deduced from speculative interpretation of geophysical (especially seismic) data if localised borehole information is not available.

Gas surveys in unsaturated soil (the 'vadose' zone) and in groundwaters (wells, springs and boreholes) are essential and relatively low-cost checks. However, the Abbeystead data for groundwaters show that no significant anomalies would have been picked up until seepages into the tunnel itself had been sampled.

Wherever there is a risk of methane from its possible entry into a tunnel in solution in groundwater, either the total exclusion of water from any part of a project which could become a potential danger should be ensured or the more practical alternative of adequate dilution and mixing, noting that at any point of disturbance, methane gas will be released from water at an accelerated rate (Orr *et al.*, 1991).

If water tunnels, pipelines and pump-housings are recognised as potential gas traps under certain conditions they should be regarded as the highest risk category of confined spaces (like sewage wells) from the point of view of entry by personnel for inspection or work.

7.4 THE GAS EXPLOSION AT LOSCOE, DERBYSHIRE

At 6.30 am on 24 March 1986 the bungalow at 51 Clarke Avenue, Loscoe, Derbyshire was completely destroyed by a methane gas explosion. The three occupants though badly injured, were lucky to escape with their lives (see Figure 26). Although natural gas was supplied to the bungalow, gas samples taken from the wreckage soon after the explosion were found to be generally similar to landfill gas which is typically composed of 60% methane and 40% carbon dioxide. Attention was drawn to a landfill whose boundary lay about 70 m from the bungalow. This landfill occupied a former brick-clay quarry in coal measures strata and had been filled between 1973 and 1982 with waste, including from 1977 onwards a large amount of domestic refuse containing biodegradable material. Shortly before the explosion, the landfill had been capped with a layer of clay which encouraged the lateral movement of bacteriogenic gas. After the explosion, boreholes were drilled to extract and flare off landfill gas to help prevent its lateral migration; trenches were also dug to ventilate the gas, but problems of high water levels and discrete pockets of waste call for other more permanent measures (Barry and Raybould, 1988).

Figure 26 *Destroyed bungalow at Loscoe. (photograph: Derby Evening Telegraph)*

A gas survey showed dangerous concentrations of methane in several adjacent houses and at least two families were evacuated. A detailed geological appraisal was made using reliable data collected by the Geological Survey while re-mapping the area in the mid-1960s (Geol. Surv. Gt. Brit., 1963). This revealed a fractured and gas-permeable sandstone horizon to be the pathway from the landfill (see Figure 27). The area was also underlain by several shallow coal seams. There was a high probability that gas was migrating through old workings in at least one of the seams exposed during the quarry operation. Subsidence of workings on up to eight other seams below the level of the quarry floor had contributed to fracturing of the near-surface strata over a wide area, enhancing the permeability of the sandstone horizon from the landfill to the housing. The ground was covered by a thin layer of impermeable clay or 'head'. Gas in the sandstone was expected to escape where this head was absent or had been breached by digging for foundations or through laying underground services.

At the time of the explosion a very deep meteorological depression was passing over the region and it is probable that this created a pressure gradient from the landfill, helping the gas to escape in large volumes into the cavity below a suspended floor. The precise means of entry was not identified, but it may have gained admittance *via* the loose brickwork surrounding a foul drainage pipe entering the building below ground. Ignition was probably by the pilot-flame of a gas central heating boiler.

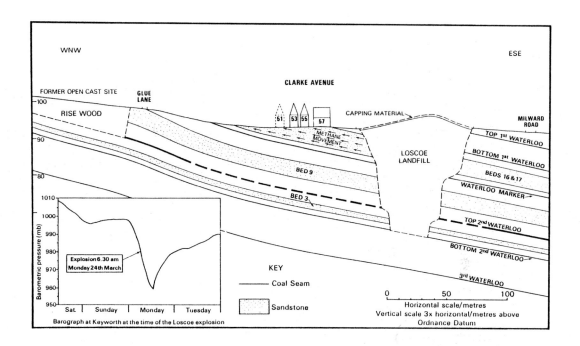

Figure 27 *Geological cross-section through the Loscoe landfill*

During the gas survey of the area, it became apparent that up to 2-3 years before the explosion there had been several reports of distressed vegetation in gardens. Typically the soil became warm, then dried out and crumbled and the lawn died. The problem reappeared even after returfing. In one garden 90 m away from the landfill, the occupier dug into a patch of lawn in an attempt to discover why it had died. An unpleasant smell 'like a sewer' was detected, along with white mould, warmth, and 'a rumbling noise like a burst pipe'. A hole was dug 0.5 m deep to expose muddy water bubbling with gas. The gas contained 50% of the lower explosive limit (LEL) of methane but no carbon monoxide was recorded. It was assumed that the gas originated from underlying coal workings or from a burning coal seam, so the occupier contacted the National Coal Board (NCB, now British Coal) who installed a standpipe with flame trap to allow the soil gas to vent harmlessly to the atmosphere. Analyses of the issuing gas suggested to the Coal Board that it was unlike mine gas which has little carbon dioxide, but was probably derived from rotting vegetable matter.

Unfortunately, the full significance of the distressed vegetation was not realised until after the explosion when boreholes were drilled to determine the cause of the heating. In one borehole there was a gradual decrease in soil temperature with depth from 20.7°C at depths of $0 - 0.5$ m below the surface to 18°C at 2.27 m below ground level. This was accompanied by an increase in methane composition from 2% at the surface to 33.4% at 2.27 m. Gas samples taken at 1.65 m in sandstone contained 29.6% nitrogen suggesting that the methane could have been mixed with air. Coal was not intercepted. If a burning coal seam were present the temperature would have been expected to increase with depth towards the coal seam. However, the reduction in temperature with depth and the absence of a coal seam was consistent with the theory that methane migrating to the surface was being oxidised, possibly by bacteria, in the soil zone. The gas below the zone of oxidation was similar to landfill gas.

The ground adjacent to the NCB standpipe was found to have a lower temperature profile with only a limited amount of carbon dioxide and methane in the soil gas atmosphere. However, gas similar in composition to that in the landfill (58% methane and 39% carbon dioxide) was encountered at 3.0 m depth in a sandstone horizon. Again, no coal was intercepted.

Further details of the Loscoe case can be found in Williams and Aitkenhead (1991).

7.5 ILLUSTRATING SOME CONSTRUCTION SCENARIOS

As noted in Section 7.2, there are few published case histories, and not all of these are described in detail. This is despite the relatively large number of investigations that have been and are being made on sites affected by methane, whether for existing developments or new projects. In order to explain the approaches which engineers adopt in dealing with methane, several hypothetical but realistic scenarios are presented below. In summary form, they illustrate the types of question which should be asked and give some of the options which can be considered for different scenarios of gas source and type of structure. The purpose is not to give a checklist — every development project has to be examined in relation to its specific situation — but to show the principal elements in addressing different types of methane hazard.

The scenarios considered are:

1. A house and landfill gas (Figure 28).

2. A house and mine gas (Figure 29).

3. A building above peat (Figure 30).

4. Tunnelling (Figure 31).

5. Dams (Figure 32).

6. Development near a gassing site (Figure 33).

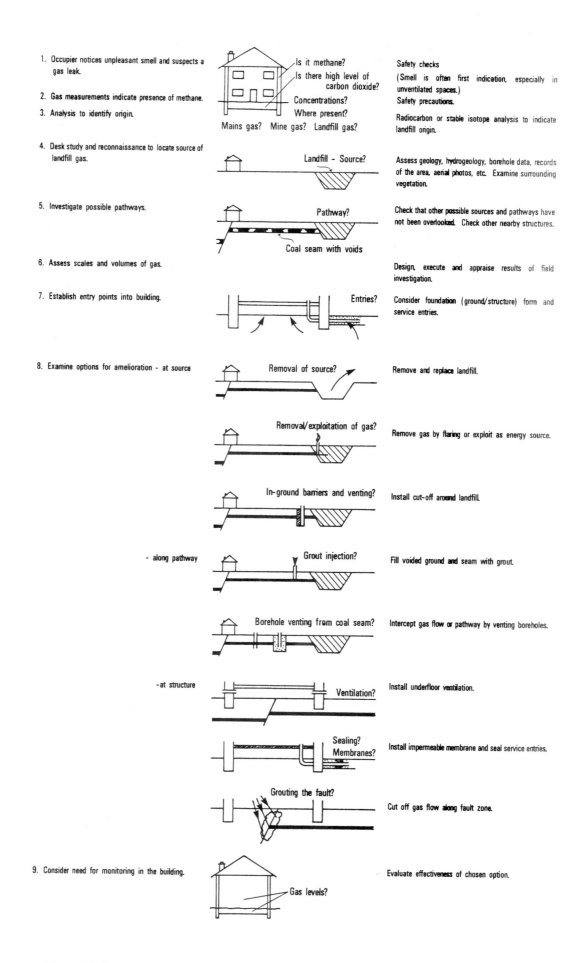

1. Occupier notices unpleasant smell and suspects a gas leak.

2. Gas measurements indicate presence of methane.

3. Analysis to identify origin.

Is it methane?
Is there high level of carbon dioxide?
Concentrations?
Where present?
Mains gas? Mine gas? Landfill gas?

Safety checks
(Smell is often first indication, especially in unventilated spaces.)
Safety precautions.

Radiocarbon or stable isotope analysis to indicate landfill origin.

4. Desk study and reconnaissance to locate source of landfill gas.

Landfill - Source?

Assess geology, hydrogeology, borehole data, records of the area, aerial photos, etc. Examine surrounding vegetation.

5. Investigate possible pathways.

Pathway?

Coal seam with voids

Check that other possible sources and pathways have not been overlooked. Check other nearby structures.

6. Assess scales and volumes of gas.

Design, execute and appraise results of field investigation.

7. Establish entry points into building.

Entries?

Consider foundation (ground/structure) form and service entries.

8. Examine options for amelioration - at source

Removal of source?

Remove and replace landfill.

Removal/exploitation of gas?

Remove gas by flaring or exploit as energy source.

In-ground barriers and venting?

Install cut-off around landfill.

- along pathway

Grout injection?

Fill voided ground and seam with grout.

Borehole venting from coal seam?

Intercept gas flow or pathway by venting boreholes.

- at structure

Ventilation?

Install underfloor ventilation.

Sealing?
Membranes?

Install impermeable membrane and seal service entries.

Grouting the fault?

Cut off gas flow along fault zone.

9. Consider need for monitoring in the building.

Gas levels?

Evaluate effectiveness of chosen option.

Figure 28 Scenario 1: a house and landfill gas

1. Gas found in under-floor spaces and wall cavities.
2. Presence of carbon dioxide as a substantial component with methane diverted attention from mine gas - methane oxidation had taken place.
3. Mineshaft had not been shown on records examined during investigation for the development and its presence had not been noted during construction works.

General points for a mining area suffering pit closures:

* In a post-mining situation, consider depths of workings, inter-connectivity of underground tunnels and voids, mining methods used ('pillar and stall' creates voids), location and size of voids and void migration.

* Investigate gas regime; does methane oxidation occur to produce a risk?

* Investigate groundwater regime; will flooding of the mine push gas towards the surface or into lateral voids?

* Consider ventilation and other protection design options for developments in high risk areas.

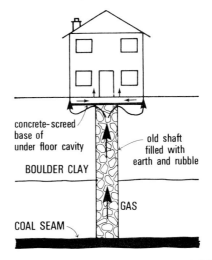

Expose and partially clear the shaft; backfill with coarse gravel and install venting pipe(s) to atmosphere; recap the shaft with concrete. Monitor to check effectiveness.

Staff et al., (1991) have reviewed the potential for surface emissions of methane from abandoned mine workings, highlighting the mechanisms of migration and detailing some case studies in North East England, Cumbria and South Yorkshire (see also Smith, 1988). A case history of landfill gas migrating through ancient coal workings and reaching the surface possibly via a fault zone, has been described by Raybould and Anderson, (1987).

Figure 29 *Scenario 2: a house and mine gas*

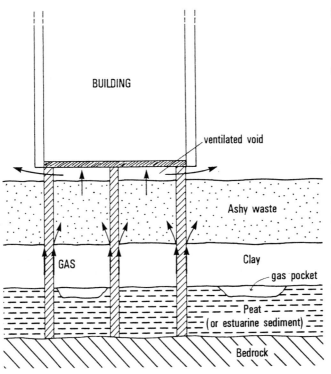

* Identify peat lenses and layers at depth by ascertaining the local geology (marsh or estuarine deposits? peat in buried channel horizons?)

* Beware methane blowout from gas pockets during piling or drilling operations.

* Piles into the peat may provide means of gas escape to the surface.

* Vibro-replacement (stone columns) used to improve the ground of the site will be pathways for gas.

* Dynamic compaction to improve the ground of the site will compress the peat and disturb the structure of the ground and the groundwater conditions.

* Consider design of ventilated void beneath building - passive or active depending on emission rates.

Figure 30 *Scenario 3: a building above peat*

Soft ground, shallow tunnels   **Hard ground, deep tunnels**

Consider possible sources of gas:

* gas from nearby landfills or estuarine deposits.
* gas from coal measures deposits or carbonaceous strata like mudstones and shales.
* gas from deep-seated hydrocarbon reservoirs.
* gas from groundwater seepage or from carried waters?

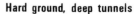
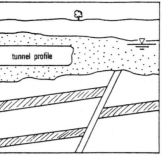
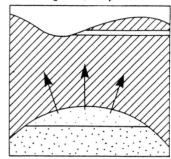

Consider possible pathways:

* gas-permeable and voided strata.
* faults.
* groundwater entries.
* groundwater level changes.

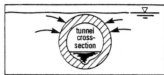

Consider methane drainage and conditions for safe working during tunnelling.

FORWARD PROBING

Consider impact of tunnel on changes in the groundwater and gas regimes of the host rocks.

Plan sampling and analysis of tunnel atmospheres and waters for gas contents at each phase of the tunnel construction process and during its operation. Take into account tunnel ventilation during excavation.

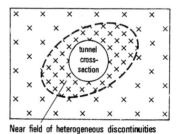

Near field of heterogeneous discontinuities with changed permeabilities

* Design out spaces for potential gas accumulation.
* Consider the lining and its back-grouting and joints for ingress and flow of fluids.

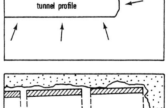

* Will shafts accumulate hazardous gases?
* Will organic matter accumulate in parts of the tunnels and drains during operation and create hazardous gas sources?

Examine possible situations in the operational phase and consider potential hazards.

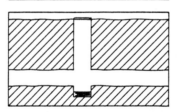

The methane studies for the Channel Tunnel project illustrated well the need for a comprehensive desk study of possible sources of methane from the rocks surrounding the proposed tunnel, especially underlying coal-bearing strata (Warren et al., 1989). Field measurements from borehole samples and from within the tunnel itself indicated that methane was not present in significant amounts. Nevertheless, comprehensive gas detection programmes were established for both the construction and operation of the tunnels. During the recent dewatering phase of the 1881 Beaumont Tunnel prior to backfilling, methane was found at up to 6% volume requiring venting; the source was attributed to the presence of creosote impregnated timber supports.

Pearson (1989, 1991) has given accounts of the precautions needed during pre-construction, construction and post-construction phases of a project. It is essential that the operating (post-construction) procedures for underground installations include a regular re-evaluation of the hazardous gas risk. There should be a sustained awareness of the potential for methane and other gases to pose a hazard. A system of feedback is required between the engineer, operator and employer to enable the engineer to assess adequately the effect of changed conditions on the level of hazard. The Health and Safety at Work, etc Act 1974, places a responsibility on all employers and employees in matters of safety.

In order to decrease the permeability of the zone of disturbance around a tunnel, grouting and the implementation of better membrane liners in gassy ground are being more widely considered (Pearson, 1991).

Pearson and Edwards (1989) highlight the problem of interpreting small amounts of methane in a ventilated tunnel; relating the volumetric flow rates of methane entering a system to the ventilation rate may reveal hazards for an operating condition involving no means of methane removal.

Figure 31 *Scenario 4: tunnelling*

* Consider sediments accumulating in the reservoir and generating marsh gas.

* If marsh gas is likely, consider possible methane transport by seepage of water into tunnels, wells and drains; consider oxidation during migration to give carbon dioxide.

* Will sedimentary sludge be deposited in tunnels, wells or drains and and become sources of hazardous gases? If so, assess risks.

* Consider nature of earth fill - are the mineral phases and carbonaceous components stable to weathering and microbial degredation?

* Check for inappropriate mix of different rock types in the earth fill e.g. limestone with pyritic mudrock.

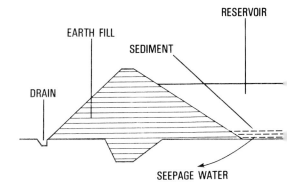

* Is there potential for methane-bearing water seepage into the bedrock and bypassing of the dam downstream? Would any nearby structures be affected?

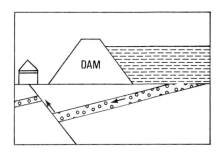

Figure 32 *Scenario 5: dams*

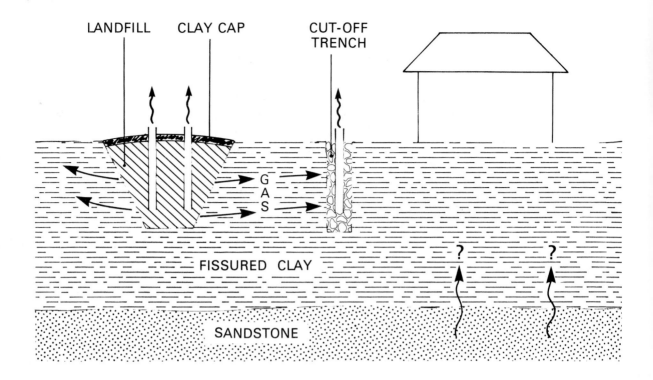

LANDFILL   CLAY CAP   CUT-OFF TRENCH

GAS

FISSURED CLAY

SANDSTONE

* Site investigation of possible gas sources and scales. What is known of the function and nature of the landfill?

* Identify potential pathways of methane movement through the ground e.g. is the permeable sandstone carrying gas? Are fissures and underground service ducts, drains and pipes gas routes?

* Will landfill leachate be a problem? Could the leachate be a source or means of transport of hazardous gases and pose a risk?

* Is the groundwater regime affecting the gas regime?

* Use all the gas measurements and information from the investigation stage in planning and designing the development.

* Consider measures to prevent lateral migration of gas. e.g. pumped borehole ventilation of waste source, grouting, the use of a cut-off trench between source and development (design appropriate depth and consider active ventilation of trench), keeping the ground between source and development free of tarmac or concrete cover i.e. unsealed.

* Consider effects of rainfall. e.g. on lateral migration of gas, ponding in cut-off trench.

* Development design considerations: internal cut-off trenches, venting pipes to roof, under-floor membrane barriers?

Barry and Raybould (1988) regarded questions such as 'how should gas migration be controlled?' and 'what is the minimum safe distance from a landfill for development?' as too generalised for sensible answers. These authors considered that there are very few sites in mining areas or elsewhere that cannot be developed safely, providing that:

* the hazard is recognised.
* appropriate desk studies and site investigations are carried out and properly interpreted.
* precautions are taken in respect of gas control and building design.
* the gas control system is appropriate for the circumstances and degree of risk, especially ground settlement.

Figure 33 *Scenario 6: development near a gassing site*

8 Thinking about methane

An awareness and technical appreciation of methane hazards are required for any civil engineering project involving construction on or in the ground. Clear thinking about methane and other gases should be sustained during the pre-construction, construction and post-construction or operational phases of the project. For underground civil engineering projects, there must always be caution in design, construction, operation and maintenance. However safe underground works appear or can be shown to be at a given time, they should always be treated as having the potential for unpredictable inflows of dangerous gases.

The practices employed in the siting and licensing of a landfill and the operational procedures of a landfill have profound influences on the surrounding environment. Predicting the consequences of location and use of a landfill in a methane risk appraisal is not easy, and requires expert interpretation and evaluation of a large set of data. Equally, when an engineer is making a site investigation for development work on contaminated land, crucial data are often missing. Information derived from comprehensive records of mining and industrial activity, placement of shafts and boreholes, landfill locations and inventories are all important. A register requirement for all new shafts and boreholes made would be of assistance for future development projects.

The influences of the ground and the hazardous gases on construction and the influences of construction processes on the environment with respect to the hazardous gases are difficult to disentangle in some scenarios. In order to clarify the view of these interacting effects, a general interaction matrix approach can be used. An interaction matrix can be used as a device to stimulate thought processes on methane hazards. The relevant primary factors employed in a 4 × 4 matrix are the gas, the ground, the groundwater and the construction. This approach (after Hudson, 1989) is a means of asking the right questions for a given construction situation and provides a starting point for defining hazardous gas problems. The matrix approach does not give prescriptive solutions but offers a way of examining a scenario from the broad scope to detailed levels, covering all stages of the construction process from investigation through to maintenance.

Confidence in a gas risk assessment depends on a good understanding of the geological, physical, chemical and biological processes that can act upon the hazardous gases in the particular circumstances of a project. Yet there are still gaps in basic research. More effective methane hazard evaluations would come from a better understanding of methane sources, gas composition changes during migration, and the mechanisms of movement, especially transport by groundwaters in the U.K. Furthermore, better gas risk assessments would result from improvements in modelling migration of landfill gas.

8.1 INTERACTIONS BETWEEN METHANE AND CONSTRUCTION

8.1.1 The interaction matrix

The interaction matrix, developed by Professor J.A. Hudson and used in his CIRIA Report (1989) entitled *Rock Mechanics Principles in Engineering Practice,* can be applied to the context of methane and construction, or indeed any problem involving interlinked factors. It is a way of stimulating clear thinking. When developing an interaction matrix, the proposed construction operation (or site or structure) occupies the bottom right hand corner of the matrix. Next the primary factors relevant to the construction situation define the main diagonal of the matrix. Finally, the evaluation of the effects of the primary factors on the construction operation, the effects of construction on the primary factors and the interactions of the primary factors on each other fill the remaining squares in the matrix. Figure 34 illustrates the algorithm for making a matrix.

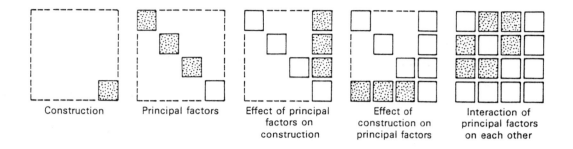

| Construction | Principal factors | Effect of principal factors on construction | Effect of construction on principal factors | Interaction of principal factors on each other |

The numbers in each box follow conventional matrix notation, i.e. the first number denotes the row and the second number the column. Note that $box_{i,j}$ does not equal $box_{j,i}$. This is equivalent to saying that the influence of factor A on B is not the same as the influence of factor B on A.

Figure 34 *Algorithm for making an interaction matrix (after Hudson, 1989)*

Primary factors relevant to methane and associated gases and their hazards to construction are:

The gas   (type(s), source, amount etc.)

The ground   (stucture, mass characteristics, pathways etc.)

The groundwater   (flow regime, solution chemistry etc.).

Additional factors could be relevant in influencing the construction site or operation, e.g. time, human activity, external agencies such as weather or environmental constraints. An illustration of the matrix approach is given in Figure 35.

8.1.2 Examples for different development situations

Three examples of interaction matrices are given to represent typical scenarios. These are:

1. Mine gas and existing developments (Figure 36).

2. Landfill gas and new nearby warehouse development (Figure 37).

3. Peat deposits and new housing (Figure 38).

The interactions put forward in these examples are some, but by no means all, of the possible conditions or situations which have to be considered.

8.1.3 Further uses of the interaction matrix

The interactive approach can be extended to different stages of the construction process, e.g.:

• investigation

• design

• construction phase

• monitoring

• operation

• maintenance.

These stages could be subdivided if required into detailed work operations or components of the structure, e.g. the inspection of an undercroft, when workers' safety is of overriding concern; or the entry of a service duct into a building.

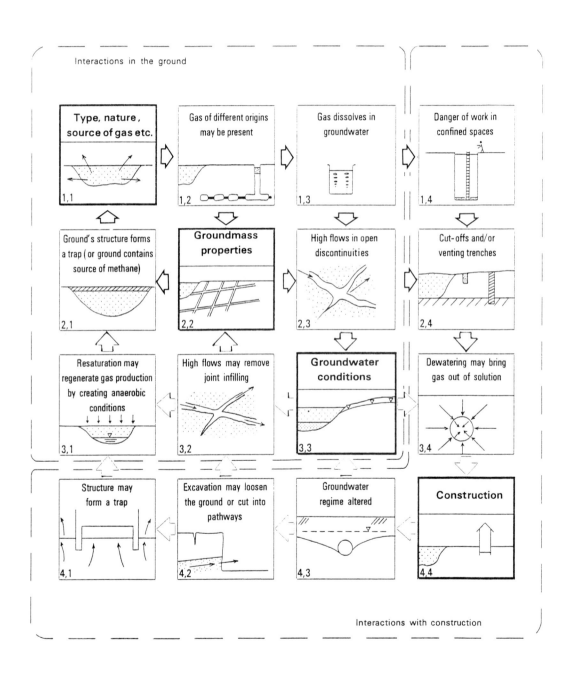

Figure 35 *Interactions: methane and construction*

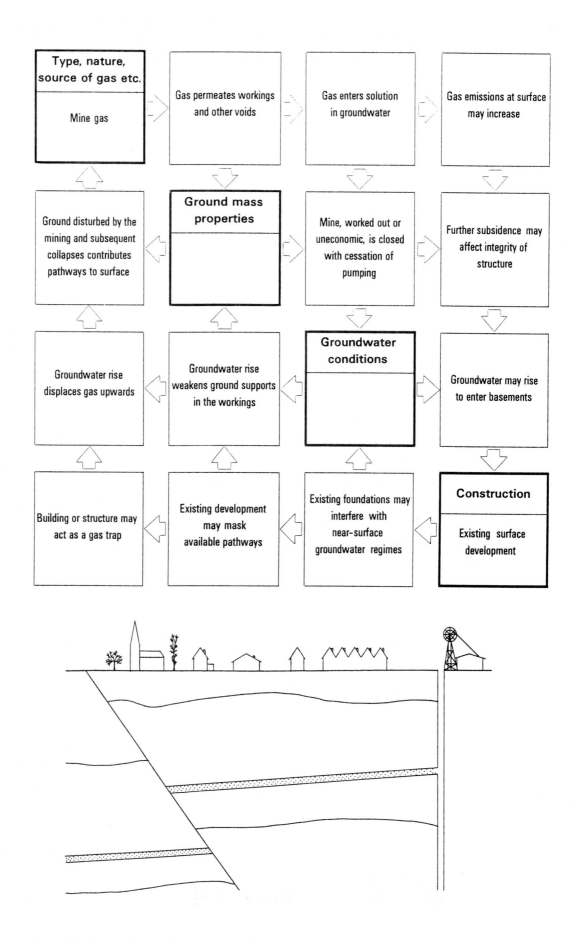

Figure 36 *Interactions: mine gas and existing developments*

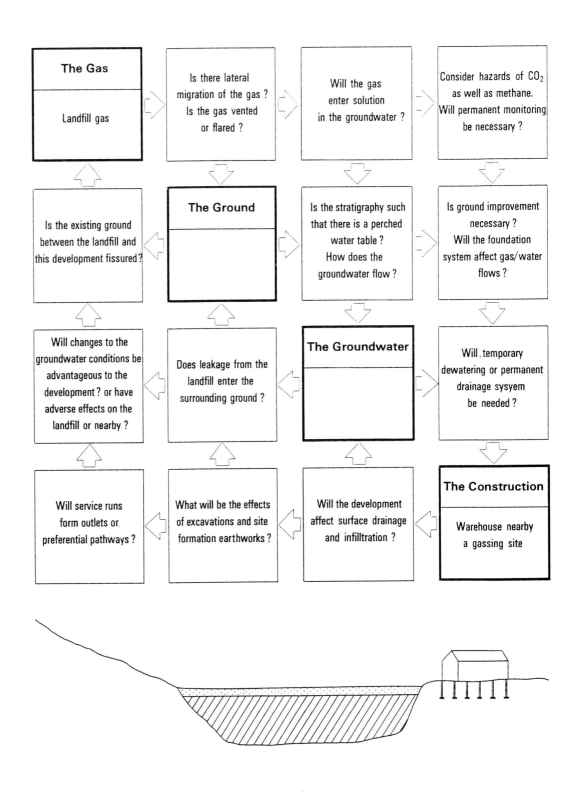

The Gas

Landfill gas

Is there lateral migration of the gas ? Is the gas vented or flared ?

Will the gas enter solution in the groundwater ?

Consider hazards of CO_2 as well as methane. Will permanent monitoring be necessary ?

Is the existing ground between the landfill and this development fissured ?

The Ground

Is the stratigraphy such that there is a perched water table ? How does the groundwater flow ?

Is ground improvement necessary ? Will the foundation system affect gas/water flows ?

Will changes to the groundwater conditions be advantageous to the development ? or have adverse effects on the landfill or nearby ?

Does leakage from the landfill enter the surrounding ground ?

The Groundwater

Will, temporary dewatering or permanent drainage sysyem be needed ?

Will service runs form outlets or preferential pathways ?

What will be the effects of excavations and site formation earthworks ?

Will the development affect surface drainage and infilltration ?

The Construction

Warehouse nearby a gassing site

Figure 37 *Interactions: landfill gas and new development*

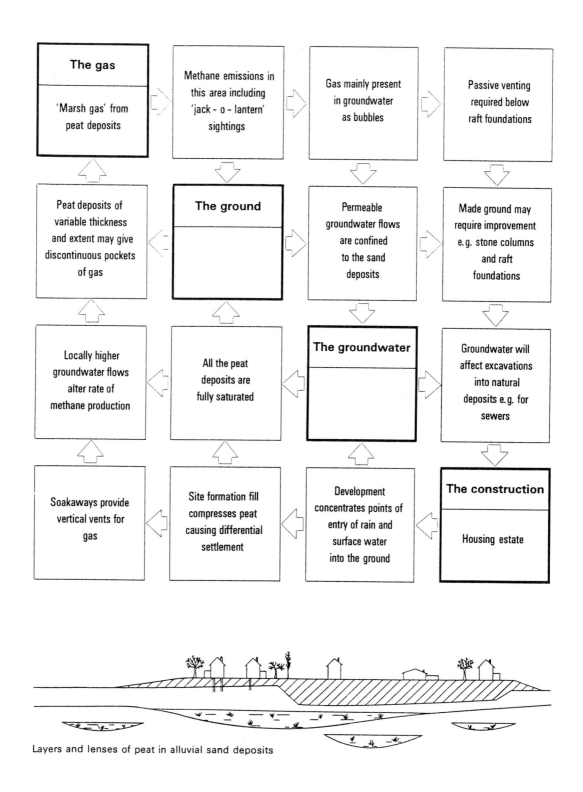

The gas

'Marsh gas' from peat deposits

Methane emissions in this area including 'jack - o - lantern' sightings

Gas mainly present in groundwater as bubbles

Passive venting required below raft foundations

Peat deposits of variable thickness and extent may give discontinuous pockets of gas

The ground

Permeable groundwater flows are confined to the sand deposits

Made ground may require improvement e.g. stone columns and raft foundations

Locally higher groundwater flows alter rate of methane production

All the peat deposits are fully saturated

The groundwater

Groundwater will affect excavations into natural deposits e.g. for sewers

Soakaways provide vertical vents for gas

Site formation fill compresses peat causing differential settlement

Development concentrates points of entry of rain and surface water into the ground

The construction

Housing estate

Layers and lenses of peat in alluvial sand deposits

Figure 38 *Interactions: marsh gas and new development*

It is equally possible to look at more general matters such as overall safety, project costs, effects on the local environment, even subjects of current uncertainty which need more research, e.g. procedures for site investigation or methods of protection of new and existing developments from methane hazards. It is conceivable, therefore, that all the relevant interaction matrices could be compiled as overlays which could be arranged in a hierarchical fashion that would not imply 3-D thinking but a means of going from the general to the particular. This arrangement is shown in Figure 39.

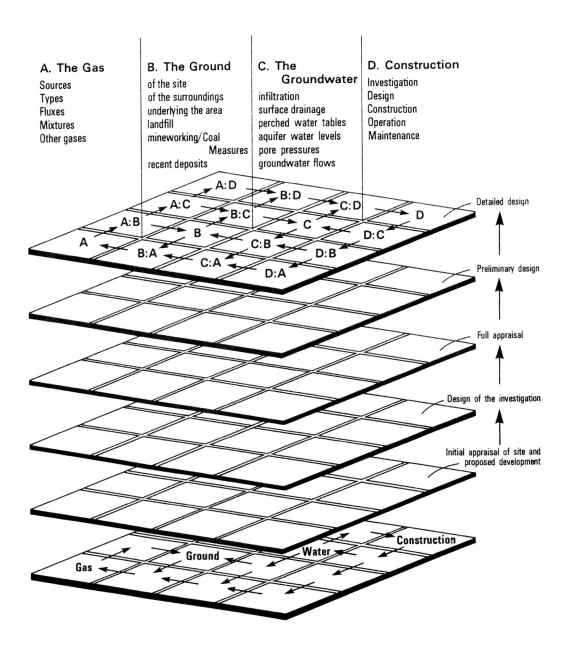

Figure 39 *Using the interaction matrix for different stages of a construction project*

Using this approach of interaction matrices does not provide solutions, nor is it the purpose of this report to do so. Each situation has its own characteristics and the appropriate solutions will depend on the particular site, the intended development and on numerous other factors. But by thinking about the interactions, by posing questions as to how to deal with them and by considering the lessons from experience, specific and appropriate solutions can be developed. The key questions can be given in the matrix form, e.g. as in Figure 40, which could be extended to a 5 × 5 matrix to include the time factor or another factor such as cost.

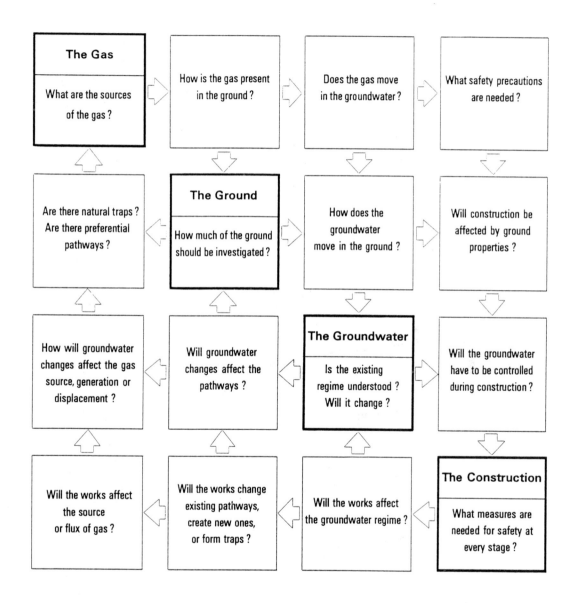

Figure 40 *Principal questions for construction in the context of methane and associated hazards*

8.2 RESEARCH NEEDS

Confidence in a gas risk assessment depends on a good understanding of the geological, physical, chemical and biological processes that can act upon the hazardous gases in the particular circumstances of a project. Yet there are still gaps in basic research, and research projects initiated by CIRIA and the DoE can only help to increase awareness and technical appreciation of methane hazards in the construction industry (see CIRIA Project Report 5 for guidance on research areas; Staff and Sceal, 1992). More effective methane hazard evaluations would come from a better understanding of methane sources, gas composition changes during migration, and the mechanisms of movement, especially transport by groundwaters. Stable isotope studies of gas source identification is a profitable area to pursue.

While some systematic surveys of methane and other gases in groundwaters have been carried out in other countries, in the UK such an attempt has not been made. In the light of the Abbeystead and Carsington methane problems, such a survey would seem appropriate, particularly in areas prone to methane hazards and where our understanding is poor. How methane is transported by groundwaters and the changes that can occur as the groundwater moves through different rock types are not well documented.

More research is needed to identify the extent of the problem of infiltration of methane-bearing groundwaters into tunnelled systems (Pearson and Edwards, 1989).

The processes surrounding the movement of landfill gas away from its source is already an area of research. The processes are complex and the specific circumstances are often important controlling factors. However, better gas risk assessments would result from improvements in our capability of modelling the migration of landfill gases. The validation of migration models through the application of field study data is an important direction to follow.

CIRIA Project Report 5 (Staff and Sceal, 1992) lists many topics of active research and many more which, according to the expert consideration of professionals experienced in dealing with methane, require further research. Many of these topics are interrelated and the need for further research is primarily in order to improve our capability to assess and control the potential risks from methane. Some of the most important research needs can be summarised as:

- hazardous gas surveys of selected groundwaters in the UK

- composition changes during migration of the gas or gas-bearing groundwater

- stable isotope and other studies of gas provenance and gas source characterisation

- ingress of gas-bearing groundwaters into tunnels

- modelling gas regimes in the ground.

The implication of these uncertainties is that designers of construction projects should take particular care when assessing the reliability of measurements or postulated models and be cautious in their interpretation of gas regimes.

Appendix A Physical properties of gases

A.1 GAS COMPOSITIONS

Table 5 The composition of air

Nitrogen	78.08 %
Oxygen	20.95 %
Argon	0.93 %
Carbon dioxide	0.03 %
Neon	0.0018 %
Helium	0.0005 %
Methane	0.00016 %
Krypton	0.0001 %
Xenon	0.00001 %

These figures represent the volume composition
of dry air at sea level (average values).
Air generally contains in addition, water vapour,
hydrocarbons, hydrogen peroxide, sulphur compounds and
dust particles in small but variable amounts.

Table 6 Compositions of gases containing methane (% vol) (after Williams and Aitkenhead,1991)

Source	CH_4	C_2H_6	C_3H_8	C_4H_{10}	*C_{2+}	CO_2	CO	N_2	O_2	Notes
Landfill	20 -65					16-57		0.5-37	< 0.3	a
Coal										
seam	80-95	8	4			0.2-6		2-9		
drainage	22-95	3	1			0.5-6	0-10	1-61		b
Anaerobic digestor	62-75					18-38		0-6		c
Natural gas										
mains	94	3.2	0.6	0.2		0.5		1.2		
general	49-99	0.7-16	0.4-7.9	0.1-3.4	0-39	0-9.5		0.1-22		
'wet'	17-97	6.4	5.3	2.6	2.1-80					
'dry'	57-98	2.0	0.6	0.3	0.1-15			4.7	0.9	
Marsh gas	11-88							3-69		
Glacial Drift	45-97				0.8-1.4	0.2-8		1.6-54		d
Deep marine biogenic	96-99				0-3					e
Estuary /lake mud										
freshwater	3-86					0.3-13		16-94		f
saltwater	55-79					2-13				

Notes:
  a composition varies with age of refuse.
  b drainage gas will be mixed with air. (Drainage gas is gas released from coal seams prior to mining as a safety
     measure.)
  c digestor waste; unspecified, animal, brewery, sewage, landfill leachate.
  d decomposition of buried peats, soils and organic rich silts deposited during terrestrial interglacial stages.
  e deep sea sediments.
  f composition varies with depth.
  * C_{2+} refers to the total volume % of hydrocarbons containing two or more carbon atoms.

A.2 GAS SOLUBILITIES

Henry's Law states that the vapour pressure of a volatile is proportional to its mole fraction in solution when the system is in equilibrium. When the partial pressure of a gas is low and its dissolved concentration is also low, this expression can be approximated adequately as:

$$p = H_a x$$

where
  p is the partial pressure of the gas (atm)
  x is the mole fraction of the gas dissolved in the aqueous phase
  H_a is the Henry's Law constant (atm/mole fraction).

The *partial pressure* of a gas is that pressure which a gas or vapour in a mixture of gases or vapours would exert if it were present alone in a vessel of the same volume as that occupied by the mixture. The *mole fraction* of a compound forming part of a mixture of compounds is the ratio of the number of molecules of the compound of interest to the total number of molecules in the mixture of compounds.

A knowledge of the solubility of a gas at one atmosphere partial pressure and known temperature allows calculation of gas solubility as pressure increases from the linear relation:

$$m = kP$$

where
  m is the mass of gas dissolved per unit volume of solvent (mg/l)
  P is the equilibrium partial pressure of the gas (atmosphere)
  k is a solubility constant at the known temperature (mg per litre of solvent per atmosphere of the gas).

For methane in water at 10°C, k is 29.9 mg per litre of water per atmosphere of methane, equivalent to 41.9 ml STP/l/atm (based on the Henry's constant in Table 7).

The solubility of methane in water at increasing depth can be roughly estimated using the following empirical relationship (Creedy, 1989):

$$V = \frac{3.2D}{(1000 + 0.36D)}$$

where V is the soluble methane content of the water on a volume per volume basis (e.g. ml/ml) at depth D in metres. This relationship assumes hydrostatic conditions and a temperature of 25°C.

Pressure, temperature and volume for an ideal gas are related by the equation of state:

$$pV = n RT$$

with p = the pressure in atmospheres
       V = the volume in ml
       n = the number of moles
       R = the gas constant = 82.056 ml atm/mol/degree
       T = temperature in Kelvin.

Gas solubilities can also be expressed using the Ostwald Coefficient, L, or the Bunsen coefficient, B:

$$L = \frac{\text{Volume of dissolved gas (at stated temperature and pressure)}}{\text{Volume of solvent (water) (at stated temperature and pressure)}}$$

$$B = \frac{\text{Volume of dissolved gas (at STP)}}{\text{Volume of solvent (water)}}$$

Table 7 Henry's Law constants for various gases in water (after Wilhelm *et al.*, 1977)

T(°C)	Air	CO_2	CO	C_2H_6	H_2	H_2S	CH_4	NO	N_2	O_2
				$H_a \times 10^{-4}$ (atm/mol fraction)						
0	4.32	0.0728	3.52	1.26	5.79	0.0268	2.24	1.69	5.29	2.55
10	5.49	0.104	4.42	12.89	6.36	0.0367	2.97	2.18	6.68	3.27
20	6.64	0.142	5.36	2.63	6.83	0.0483	3.76	2.64	8.04	4.01
30	7.71	0.186	6.20	3.42	7.29	0.0609	4.49	3.10	9.24	4.75
40	0.70	0.211	6.96	4.24	7.51	0.0743	5.20	3.52	10.1	5.15
50	9.46	0.281	7.61	5.00	7.65	0.0881	5.77	3.90	11.1	5.88
60	10.1	0.341	8.21	5.63	7.65	0.103	6.26	4.18	12.0	6.29
70	10.5		8.45	6.23	7.61	0.119	6.66	4.38	12.5	6.63
80	10.7		8.45	6.61	7.55	0.135	6.82	4.48	12.6	6.87
90	10.8		8.46	6.87	7.51	0.144	6.92	4.52	12.6	6.99
100	10.7		8.46	6.92	7.45	0.148	7.01	4.54	12.6	7.01

Table 8 Ostwald coefficients for selected gases in water at 1 atmosphere partial pressure (after Wilhelm *et al.*, 1977)

	10°C	25°C	40°C	55°C	75°C
Rn	0.3576	0.2268	0.1636	0.1313	0.1123
H_2	0.02033	0.01913	0.01887	0.01935	
N_2	0.01959	0.01588	0.01400	0.01318	0.01346
O_2	0.03960	0.03111	0.02650	0.02417	0.02332
CO	0.03195	0.02334	0.02022	0.01869	0.01825
CO_2	1.238	0.8280	0.6053	0.4768	0.3818
CH_4	0.04491	0.03395	0.02800	0.02482	0.02317
C_2H_6	0.06910	0.04530	0.03373	0.02793	0.02486
NH_3	406.6	312.7	236.0	175.8	117.0
H_2S	3.562	2.510	1.925	1.584	

Tables 7 and 8 list Henry's Law constants (in atm/mole fraction) and Ostwald coefficients (volume/volume) for different gases at temperatures up to 100°C. For more detailed explanations of the temperature and pressure dependence of gas solubilities the reader is referred to texts on physical chemistry e.g. Moore (1981); Stumm and Morgan (1981); and to research literature (e.g. Colt, 1983; Yamamoto *et al.*, 1976).

A.3 GAS VISCOSITIES

The viscosity μ_m of a mixture of gases is given by:

$$\mu_m = \frac{\Sigma \mu_i y_i M_i}{\Sigma y_i M_i} \quad \text{(for } i = 1 \text{ to } m)$$

where

$\mu_m =$ the viscosity of the mixture (centipoise)
$\mu_i =$ the viscosity of the ith component
$M_i =$ the molecular weight of the ith component
$y_i =$ the mole fraction of the ith component
$m =$ the total number of components in the mixture ($m = 2$ for a methane/carbon dioxide mixture).

For a more detailed explanation of gas viscosity in relation to other gas properties the reader is referred to Amyx *et al.* (1960). Figure 41 shows the variations in the viscosities of different gases as a function of temperature at constant atmospheric pressure.

A.4 METHANE DIFFUSION COEFFICIENTS

Table 9 Diffusion coefficients for methane in various media at 20°C (after Williams and Aitkenhead, 1991)

Medium	Diffusion coefficient m²/s
Air	1.5×10^{-5}
Water	1.49×10^{-9}
Coal — intact core	$\approx 10^{-9}$
Cemented sandstone — water saturated	$\approx 10^{-10}$
Sandstone — unsaturated	1.04×10^{-8}
Shale — water saturated	2.12×10^{-10}
CO_2 in air	1.39×10^{-5}

A.5 LIMITING CONCENTRATIONS OF GASEOUS CONTAMINANTS

Table 10 Limiting concentrations of gaseous contaminants (after Building Research Establishment, 1977)

Contaminant	Limiting concentrations	
	Toxicity or asphyxiation vol %	Explosive limits in air vol %
Methane	30	5.0 — 15.0
Carbon dioxide	0.5	
Carbon monoxide	0.005	12.0 — 75.0
Sulphur dioxide	0.0005	
Hydrogen sulphide	0.0001	4.4 — 45.0
Hydrogen	30	4.0 — 74.0
Propane	30	2.0 — 9.5
Butane	30	1.5 — 8.5
Acetylene	30	2.5 — 82.0
Petrol	0.10	1.4 — 7.6

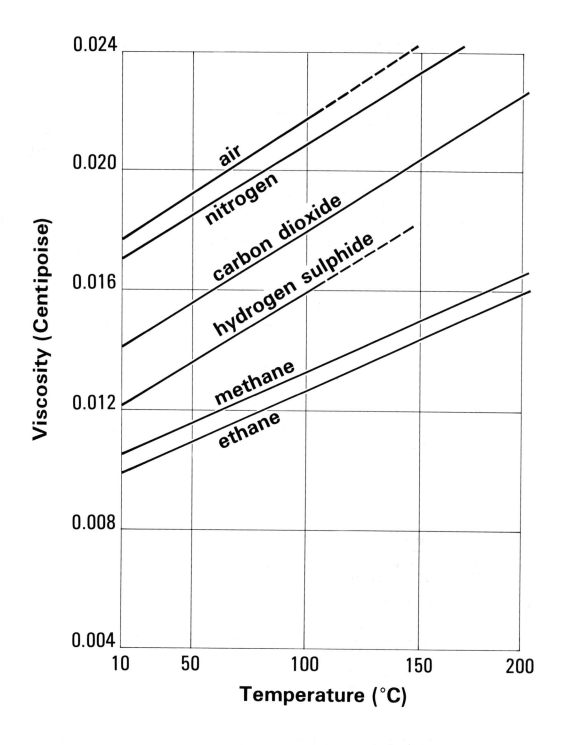

Figure 41 *Viscosity of gases at atmospheric pressure and different temperatures (after Amyx et al., 1960)*

Appendix B Volcanic and other geological sources of methane

B.1 VOLCANIC GASES

The compositions of volcanic gases derived from magma, depend upon the compositions of the magma. Gases evolved in basaltic and andesitic volcanism, like hydrothermal gases, are generally dominated by water vapour and carbon dioxide, but sulphur dioxide and nitrogen are also important; minor amounts of hydrogen, hydrogen sulphide, carbon monoxide, methane, argon (and other noble gases), sulphur (S_2), sulphur trioxide and chlorine also occur (e.g. Naughton et al., 1963; Heald et al., 1963; Gerlach and Nordlie, 1975; Gerlach, 1980a). Methane is generally rare, typically forming less than 0.1 mol % (equivalent to volume %) of the total gas (see Table 11).

Table 11 Gases from Mount St Helens volcano (after Barnes, 1984)

	Soda Spring	Govt. Mineral Spring	CO_2 well	Pigeon Spring	Dry gas from crack*	Dry gas from fumarole	Plume above another large fumarole+
O_2	0.17	0.03	0.22	0.55	0.03	18.1	21.09
Ar	0.02	<0.02	0.02	0.14	<0.02	0.82	0.92
N_2	1.10	0.60	0.83	99.44	1.64	68.4	78.47
CO_2	98.70	99.25	99.03	0.06	86.6	11.1	0.113
CO					0.57	0.07	
CH_4	0.12	<0.002	0.11	<0.005	<0.002	<0.002	<0.001
C_2H_6	<0.01	<0.01	<0.01	<0.05	<0.01	<0.01	<0.01
H_2	<0.01	<0.01	<0.01	<0.02	8.61	1.74	0.007
He	<0.02	<0.02	<0.02	<0.02	<0.005	<0.005	<0.01
H_2S					2.09	0.21	<0.001
SO_2					0.84	0.40	0.003
Totals	100.11	99.88	100.10	100.19	100.4	100.8	100.6
$\delta^{13}CO_2$	−13.1	−14.0	−5.4		−10.5	−10.8	−10.7
$\delta^{13}CO_2$	31.8	31.8	27.4				19.4
$\delta D\ H_2O$							−97.9

Compositions in volume %
* The gas from the crack is between 80 and 87% steam
+ Odour of hydrogen suplhide, strong odour of 'SO$_2$' and physiologically 'very hot'.

The oxidation state of volcanic gases is a function of temperature and, accordingly, the nature of the carbon- and sulphur-bearing species varies with temperature. Theoretical modelling of gases in the C-O-H-S system at temperatures above 800°C and at oxygen fugacities (i.e. partial pressures of chemical availability of oxygen, typically 10^{-10} atm) characteristic of basaltic lavas, indicates hydrocarbons of any sort would be virtually non-existent (Gerlach and Nordlie, 1975; MacDonald, 1983). Similarly, Gerlach (1980a) concluded that closed-system cooling of typical Hawaiian volcanic gases would give methane concentrations of less than 10^{-10} mol % at pressures of 1−100 bars. It is therefore probable that the small amounts of methane (0.01−0.05%) which have occasionally been reported for volcanic gas samples at temperatures above 600°C (e.g. Heald et al., 1963), resulted from organic matter contamination (Gerlach, 1980a). However, Gerlach also concluded that if the volcanic gases equilibrate with the rock so that oxygen fugacities are buffered by the minerals present (quartz-fayalite-magnetite), then methane abundances of 5−35% are possible at 1−100 bars and at temperatures of less than 300°C, although even in this case, carbon dioxide will be the most abundant carbon-bearing species (Heald et al., 1963).

Above about 1100 °K, sulphur dioxide is the most abundant sulphur-bearing species, but below this temperature, hydrogen sulphide is most abundant (Heald et al., 1963; Naughton et al., 1963; Gerlach and Nordlie, 1975).

In acidic (siliceous) magmas halogens, especially chlorine, might be present. Since chlorine will react with water to produce hydrochloric acid, liberating oxygen, gases from acidic rock melts are likely to be more oxidizing than gases from their basaltic counterparts, and therefore carbon dioxide is more stable thermodynamically than methane. Volcanic gases from the intermediate to acid magmas of Mount Saint Helens, U.S.A., gave condensates which were up to 0.2 M HCl, but the gases were never more than 0.12 mol % methane, and carbon dioxide was by far the most abundant gaseous component (see Table 11), comprising about 99% of the total (Barnes, 1984). Organo-halogens (e.g. C_2F_2, $CHClF_2$, CH_3Cl, $CHCl_2F$ and CCl_3F) which are found in volcanic gases from basaltic and andesitic volcanoes at ppb (parts per billion, 10^9, by volume) to ppm concentrations are derived from sedimentary organic matter (Gerlach, 1980a).

Methane is therefore not likely to be a major hazard in volcanic areas producing tholeiitic or calc-alkaline magmas. However, methane can be important in alkaline magmatic provinces and theory predicts that at temperatures of less than 600°C, with oxygen levels buffered by the rock, methane abundances should increase rapidly reaching 45-75% of the gases at 200°C (Gerlach, 1980b). Localities where methane occurs in association with alkaline igneous rocks are found in the East African Rift. For example, the Nyiragongo volcano of the East African Rift, Zaire, is made up of highly alkaline sodic melilite-nepheline basalts with potassium-rich nepheline ($Na_{0.6}K_{0.4}AlSiO_4$). A continuously active ultrapotassic molten lava lake existed at Nyiaragongo from 1948 to 1977 and analyses of gases collected from this lava lake in 1959 were reported in Gerlach (1980b). Although no methane was detected, theoretical considerations led Gerlach (1980b) to suggest that the high temperature, carbon dioxide-rich, low total sulphur gases should equilibrate to produce methane at low temperatures. The calculations of Gerlach (1980b) are consistent with the findings of Burke (1963) who found deep water from Lake Kivu, on the southern flanks of Nyiragongo, to contain methane in exploitable concentrations: water at 400 m depth contained 2000 ml gas/l, consisting of 22% methane and 77% carbon dioxide. Since there are relatively small amounts of sedimentary organic matter in the lake, Burke (1963) concluded that the methane was of volcanic origin. However, Schoell et al. (1988) used stable isotope determinations to demonstrate convincingly a dual bacterial origin for the methane; one-third of the methane in Lake Kivu is produced by an acetate fermentation process; the remaining two-thirds are derived from reduction of carbon dioxide by bacteria using dissolved magmatic carbon dioxide introduced into the lake through hydrothermal vents.

Volcanic activity often produces large amounts of carbon dioxide e.g. in 1986 there was a catastrophic release of carbon dioxide from Lake Nyos, which fills a collapsed volcanic caldera in Cameroon. The gas burst from the lake forming a cloud which claimed the lives of 1700 people by asphyxiation (Anderson, 1987). The carbon dioxide had accumulated gradually in the lower waters of the lake as the volcano degassed; an instability in the lake water structure probably triggered the sudden release of the dissolved gases from solution when the bottom layers rose to the surface and attained lower hydrostatic pressures.

In volcanic/hydrothermal environments, dissolved CO_2-, H_2S- and SO_2-dominated gases may result in low pH i.e. acid waters which may be hazardous to the construction industry. Dissolved carbon dioxide-dominated gases in Lake Nyos give a pH as low as 3.5 (Oskarsson, 1990). Similarly, acid gases from the Nevado Del Ruiz volcano of Colombia give rise to waters with pH as low as 2.8 (Giggenbach et al., 1990).

B.2 HYDROTHERMAL AND GEOTHERMAL SOURCES

Hydrothermal/geothermal systems, in which hot, aqueous fluids convect at temperatures up to 350°C, have developed in a wide range of lithologies, in a wide variety of areas where geothermal gradients are high, usually above and in response to deep-seated magmatic activity.

Such systems may be subaqueous or subaerial, oceanic or continental. Methane can be produced from several carbon sources under a wide variety of conditions in all types of hydrothermal system. Methane can be evolved from existing organic molecules or synthesised from inorganic molecules at high temperatures; methane with the latter origins may be termed 'abiogenic'. Carbon dioxide is the main gas constituent, being present at high partial pressures in solution and as a component of the steam-dominated gas phase in hydrothermal areas. Thermogenic methane in hydrothermal systems is likely to be much less of a hazard to the construction industry than the other species present, especially sulphur dioxide and hydrogen sulphide, which can lead to acid conditions, with pH as low as 1 (Henley *et al.*, 1984).

Continental hydrothermal systems are likely to be of greatest concern to the construction industry. In these carbon dioxide is typically the most abundant carbon-bearing species, often composing over 90 % of the total gas (excluding water vapour), while in addition hydrogen sulphide and hydrogen are often more abundant than methane. However, methane is typically the most abundant hydrocarbon. Usually concentrations of carbon dioxide increase regularly with temperature, suggesting that its abundance is controlled by mineral-fluid equilibria, whereas methane concentrations show no such simple trend (Arnórsson and Gunnlaugsson, 1985). This latter observation implies that either methane concentrations are not controlled by mineral-fluid equilibria, or else that methane from different origins is typically mixed in these hydrothermal systems (Welhan, 1988).

Stable isotope and compositional evidence is consistent with methane in most continental hydrothermal systems being of thermogenic origin (Welhan, 1988). The $\delta^{13}C$ values of geothermal methanes lie between -30 ‰ and -20 ‰, and are similar to coal gases in NW Europe, but their deuterium (^2H) contents are consistently lower with δ^2H values ranging from -25 ‰ to -275 ‰ (relative to Standard Mean Ocean Water, SMOW). (See Section 4.4 and Appendix C for an explanation of the stable isotope terms.) It is worth mentioning that carbon-13 fractionation between methane and carbon dioxide may be a significant process at high temperatures. In some instances, low temperature bacterial oxidation of pre-existing thermogenic methane results in methane much heavier in its stable isotopes of ^{13}C and ^2H. This occurs in the Salton Sea geothermal system in the Imperial Valley, California, where shallow, warm gases have $\delta^{13}C$ values in the range -16.3 ‰ to -0.6 ‰ and δ^2H values in the range -180 ‰ to -16 ‰ (Barker and Fritz, 1981b).

In many geothermal systems (e.g. Cerro Prieto, New Mexico; Norte, Baja California; The Geysers Geothermal field, California; Steamboat Springs, Nevada; and the Yellowstone National Park, Wyoming), the quantities of the higher hydrocarbons, relative to methane, are greatly in excess of that expected for a mixture at equilibrium (Des Marais and Truesdell, 1987). In general, the $\delta^{13}C$ values of the hydrocarbons increase with molecular weight, again consistent with these gases being produced principally by the thermocatalytic decomposition i.e. pyrolysis or 'cracking', of the larger organic compounds, including kerogen (Des Marais and Truesdell, 1987). Hydrocarbons from sedimentary geothermal aquifers (such as Cerro Prieto in Mexico, Larderello in Italy and The Geysers, California) are characterised by the presence of branched C_{4-6} molecules and a lack of unsaturated compounds other than benzene, relatively large amounts of which may be characteristic of high-temperature geothermal systems (Nehring and Fausto, 1979).

Boiling in hydrothermal systems influences the nature of the gases evolved. For example, in the producing geothermal field of Cerro Prieto, exploitation by man has caused boiling in the reservoir which has locally increased the gas content of the fluid (Nehring and Amore, 1984). The hydrocarbon gases present in the steam from Cerro Prieto closely resemble the hydrocarbons found in steam from natural gas-dominated systems such as Larderello, Italy and the Geysers, California (Nehring and Fausto, 1979). In addition, faults influence boiling and hence gas contents of the reservoir fluid (Nehring and Amore, 1984). At Cerro Prieto, enhanced gas contents of more than 2.0×10^{-3} mole fraction of the total reservoir fluid occur in boiling zones: away from the boiling zones, gas mole fractions are typically less than 1.5×10^{-3}. The produced gas is typically $1 - 5$ mol % methane, although invariably carbon dioxide is the most abundant gas (Nehring and Amore, 1984).

Hydrothermal gases from geothermal systems with reservoirs in volcanic rocks are also dominated by carbon dioxide. For example, in the Orakeikorako field of New Zealand, the reservoir rocks are a sequence of ignimbrites and pumaceous tuffs; the gas compositions are very similar to those from other New Zealand sites with volcaniclastic reservoir rocks e.g Wairakei, Waikate and Te Kopia (Sheppard and Lyon, 1984).

Submarine hydrothermal systems are unlikely to be of much concern to the construction industry. However, one such system, the Guaymas Basin System of the Gulf of California, has received considerable attention and studies of this system have shed light upon the processes which might lead to methane generation in hydrothermal systems (Initial Reports of the DSDP leg 64, 1982; Simoneit, 1985; Simoneit *et al.*, 1988; Kvenvolden and Simoneit, 1990). The Guaymas Basin system is a ridge-crest, submarine hydrothermal system overlain by immature sediments which are rich in microbial detritus. Hydrothermal fluids of marine origin at temperatures of about 315°C easily degrade the organic matter to yield petroleum-like products. This system represents a geologically fast (less than 500,000 years) mechanism for the thermal maturation of organic rich sediments to petroleum. In addition to petroleum, thermogenic hydrocarbon gas, hydrogen sulphide (detected by odour) and highly variable quantities of carbon dioxide have been identified. Thermocatalysis of organic carbon in the sediments above the hydrothermal system has produced light hydrocarbon gases (methane to pentane). Values of $\delta^{13}C_{PDB}$ (i.e. relative to the standard Peedee belemnite; see Appendix C) for methane lie in the range -43 to -51 ‰, consistent with a thermogenic origin. The light organic gases are dominated by methane (over 90% of the total gas) which constitutes up to 152 ml STP/kg of sediment fluid (Welhan and Lupton, 1987). Concentrations of carbon dioxide decrease with depth in the system, while methane abundances increase and with increasing depth/temperature the $\delta^{13}C$ values for the methane become heavier.

In addition to generation by thermogenesis at normal hydrothermal temperatures, methane can also be produced abiogenically. Abiogenesis represents the predominant methane source in high temperature (much greater than 500°C), rock-dominated mid-ocean-ridge hydrothermal systems (Welhan, 1988). Methane may be derived through outgassing, either directly from magma or due to leaching from rock, or during high temperature inorganic reactions e.g.

$$CO_2 + 4H_2 = CH_4 + 2H_2O$$

Such a methane source is quantitatively insignificant in the accessible parts of the Earth (Schoell, 1988) and its occurrence is remote from the construction industry.

B.3 SERPENTINISATION

In areas where mafic or ultramafic rocks (i.e. mantle-type rocks, poor in silica but rich in ferromagnesian minerals) are undergoing serpentinisation, i.e. low-temperature (typically less than 150°C) late-stage hydrothermal alteration, very reducing conditions can be obtained causing the hydrolysis of water, the oxidation and hydration of the ferrous-iron-bearing phases and the production of hydrogen and methane. The inorganic reaction may be symbolised as follows:

$$15FeO_{(silicates)} + 3H_2O + CO_2 = 5Fe_3O_4 + H_2 + CH_4$$
$$\text{magnetite}$$

The availability of the carbon source (in this case dissolved carbon dioxide) in the groundwater or rock dictates the eventual ratio of hydrogen to methane. If the Fe(II) is present as olivine, the mineral products of serpentinisation would include serpentine and brucite as well as magnetite.

Neal and Stanger (1983) have reported the abiogenic or inorganic production of methane in calcium-rich alkaline groundwaters (pH 10 − 12) flowing from ultramafic rocks of the Oman ophiolite, a segment of uplifted oceanic crust which makes up the Semail mountains in Oman.

Here gases emerge along fault and shear discontinuities in partly to wholly serpentinised ultramafic rock. Gases vary from almost pure hydrogen to almost pure nitrogen, with methane usually less than 4.5%. In addition, trace amounts of light organic gases from C2-C4 occur. Hydrogen is exceedingly deuterium depleted, consistent with low temperature formation at $20 - 50°C$. Gas flows vary from barely detectable to about 10 ml/s, but more substantial flows of greater than 10 l/s are reported for one site. After oxygen depletion in the groundwater, two key Fe(II) oxidation reactions can take place with the help of a catalyst e.g. a nickel-iron alloy surface, to produce hydrogen:

$$2Fe(OH)_2 \;=\; Fe_2O_3 \;+\; H_2O \;+\; H_2$$
$$\text{haematite}$$

$$3Fe(OH)_2 \;=\; Fe_3O4 \;+\; 2H_2O \;+\; H_2$$

Other areas of the world with ultramafic iron-rich rock bodies which are subject to serpentinisation and abiogenesis of gas including methane, have been described in New Zealand (Lyon et al., 1990) and in the Zambales Ophiolite of the Philippines (Abrajano et al., 1988).

B.4 METHANE FROM IGNEOUS ROCKS

Measurements of gases from pores in igneous rocks are reported in Petersil'ye and Pripachkin (1979). Calc-alkaline rocks were reported by these workers to contain from 0.4 to 9.5 ml/kg, with the lowest gas content in granitoids. In these cases hydrogen was by far the dominant gas. In contrast, however, alkali igneous rocks contain in addition to hydrogen hydrocarbons, among which methane is dominant. Methane is present in alkali rocks in concentrations from 0.002 up to 49 ml/kg, the highest noted by Petersil'ye and Pripachkin (1979) for igneous rocks.

Vast volumes of basaltic lava are extruded on to the sea floor along the mid-ocean ridges where magma is spreading out to form new oceanic crust. These fresh submarine lavas often cool under sea water pressures that are large enough to retain the gases trapped within vesicles of the glassy rock. Gas concentrations (mostly carbon dioxide) are often so high that when basaltic samples are dredged and brought to the surface of the ship, they undergo violent degassing because of the pressure drop; as the vesicles 'pop', some have been observed to bounce around the deck (Pineau et al., 1976). These and similar rocks come from the ocean mantle and are studied (e.g. Craig and Lupton, 1981) to reveal their trace element constituents and so illuminate the geochemical history of the mantle source regions.

B.5 METHANE FROM FLUID INCLUSIONS

Of possible concern to the construction industry is the occurrence of methane in fluid inclusions within mineral veins and rock-forming minerals. Studies of fluid inclusions contained in minerals suggest that some parts of the deep crust, particularly those where high temperature metamorphism of organic sediments has occurred, have methane rather than carbon dioxide as the dominant fluid (Roedder, 1984; Shepherd et al., 1985). Vein minerals (especially quartz, but to a lesser degree calcite) often contain methane inclusions (Van den Kerkhof, 1988). This is particularly the case where veins formed in organic-rich host rocks at temperatures between about 200 and 250°C (Mullis, 1987). Although it is difficult to quantify the likely abundances of methane present in mineral veins, it is possible that where veining is sufficiently intense, dangerous quantities of methane might be liberated during operations such as mining and tunnelling.

Highly tectonized Valanginian Marl in the Helvetic Nappes of the Swiss Alps contains significant amounts of methane, particularly trapped within fluid inclusions in calcite veins (Gautschi et al., 1990). The calcite veins contain up to 3 litres STP of hydrocarbon gas per litre of calcite; the coexisting helium is radiogenic and therefore derived from the crust alone, probably during the peak of the Alpine orogeny. It has been calculated that the total residuum of trapped methane in a cubic kilometre of marl containing veins is around $100 - 300 \times 10^6$ m³ STP (Gautschi et al., 1990).

B.6 METHANE HYDRATES

A major reservoir of methane in the Earth's crust takes the form of methane hydrate deposits. Estimates of the global abundance of carbon in gas hydrates (mainly methane, but including hydrates of other light organic gases) vary from 2×10^{12} to 4×10^{15} tonnes (Kvenvolden, 1988); these quantities are orders of magnitude higher than the conventional recoverable sources of methane. Natural gas hydrates are composed mainly of methane and ice; if all the sites in the clathrate molecular framework are filled with methane molecules, a unit volume of hydrate will contain about 170 volumes of methane gas at STP (MacDonald, 1983). Methane hydrates are known to occur in marine sediments at water depths greater than about 300 m (see Figure 42), particularly on continental slopes, and in Arctic areas where permafrost occurs, both on-shore and off-shore (see Figure 43). Land temperature profiles suggest that hydrates might be present to depths of 2000 m. The hydrates are a hazard to drilling operations in areas such as Alaska, where depressurisation upon drilling can lead to gas evolution. Stable isotopic studies have shown that the ultimate origin of the methane is mostly bacteriogenic (Ridley and Dominic, 1988). However, methane hydrates also occur in association with gas fields, for example in Siberia (Kvenvolden, 1988), and hence in view of the predominantly thermogenic origin of natural gases, it is likely that some of the methane in hydrates is of thermogenic origin.

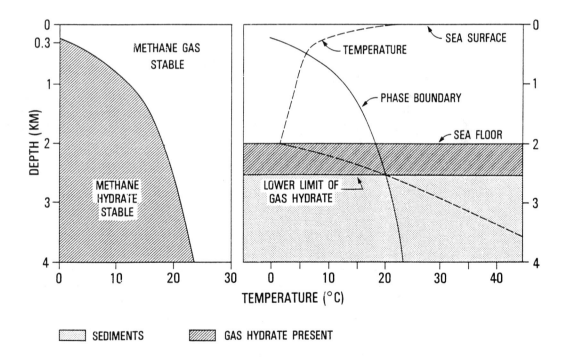

Figure 42 *(Left) Phase boundary for methane in sea water. (Right) Gas hydrate stability for the region off the southeastern United States — gas hydrates will be stable within the seafloor sediments down to a subbottom depth of about 500m (after Dillon and Paull, 1983)*

B.7 METHANE FROM FAULTS

Methane can emanate from faults in some parts of the world, for example in Japan (Sugisaki et al., 1980). Earth movements during earthquakes can lead to gas emissions, particularly along faults, and anomalous amounts of methane and hydrogen sulphide are produced in areas with coal, petroleum or organic-rich strata, while carbon dioxide is associated with limestone strata (Roshoff, 1989). The concentrations of these gases may increase or decrease prior to a seismic event, but in any event anomalies are restricted to areas close to the epicentre (Roshoff, 1989).

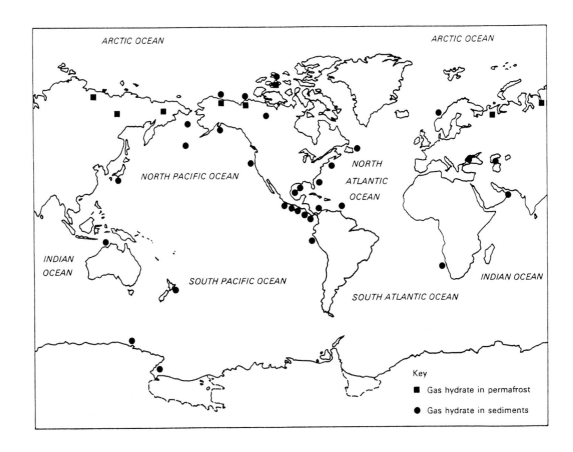

Figure 43 *The Earth showing locations of known and inferred gas hydrates in oceanic sediment of outer continental margins and in permafrost regions (after Kvenvolden, 1988)*

Carbon dioxide-rich springs containing 1000 ppm or more of bicarbonate occur world-wide along major zones of seismicity, most notably along the San Andreas fault zone in California (Irwin and Barnes, 1980). In central Japan, gases charged within fault gouges are characterised by high concentrations of hydrogen (0 − 8000 ppm) and carbon dioxide (0.05 − 1 %) and lack methane, but in contrast, gases discharged from mineral waters flowing from fault zones show high helium concentrations (up to 800 ppm), high methane contents (up to 30 mol %) and lack carbon dioxide (Sugisaki *et al.*, 1980). In the case of the carbon dioxide-rich gases, there is a correlation between carbon dioxide concentrations and degree of brecciation. Although Sugisaki *et al.* (1980) are not specific regarding the origin of these gases, they do suggest a deep origin. These workers are similarly non-specific regarding the origins of the methane-dominated gases, but note that their occurrence is correlated with the presence of underlying granite. It was considered by Sugisaki *et al.* (1983) that the gas compositions are controlled by the lithologies cut by the faults, with carbon dioxide having an organic, sedimentary or magmatic origin. Hydrogen was thought to be formed along active faults by reaction of freshly pulverised rock with water.

In fault zones around the Median Tectonic Line of Shikoku Island, Japan, carbon dioxide-rich gases (up to 90 % or more carbon dioxide) with relatively high methane/argon ratios (up to 2.1×10^{-4}) are common in the Sambagawa schist zone (Kawabe et al., 1981). The concentration of methane was considered to be controlled by the presence of graphite-rich schist.

B.8 METHANE FROM DEEP CONTINENTAL BOREHOLES

Although methane production in the 'accessible' shallow crust is dominated by that from sediment burial, there is evidence that methane of abiogenic origins is a significant fluid in some areas of older stable crust. The 'Shields' in Canada and Fenno-Scandinavia are regions of outcropping polymetamorphic Precambrian rock. In both Canada and Finland, deep boreholes associated with mining have substantial amounts of methane dissolved in the groundwater; it is not clear whether the pressures of methane ever rise to give local gas-phase accumulations at in-situ pressure and temperature. Outgassing from exploration boreholes drilled from deep base metal mines in Canada produces a free gas phase with up to 89% methane, associated with helium (up to 19%), hydrogen (up to 30%), argon (up to 5%) and nitrogen (up to 80%) (Fritz et al., 1987; Sherwood et al., 1988). A drillhole at a mine at Sudbury in Ontario evolved 15 litres every hour, 4 of which were hydrogen. Similar phenomena are found in deep boreholes in Finland (Sherwood Lollar et al., 1989) and in the 'superdeep' borehole to over 12 000 m depth at Kola in the U.S.S.R. (Kozlovsky, 1984). The origin of the methane in the Canadian Shield mine gases is not clear, but reactions of the Fischer-Tropsch type involving catalytic synthesis at about 125°C could occur:

$$nCO_2 + (3n+1)H_2 = C_nH_{2n+2} + 2nH_2O.$$

The supply of hydrogen could have been by hydrolysis or radiolytic decomposition of water. Alternatively, serpentinisation type reactions could be operating under the reducing conditions that most likely prevail at depth.

In April 1989, a 4,000 m deep borehole was completed in the Bavarian Oberpfalz region near the village of Windischeschenbach in Germany, almost in the centre of Europe, at the western edge of the Bohemian Massif. At depths greater than 3,900 m, the basement metamorphic rocks contained highly saline water with a gas content of 800 ml/l, comprising 70% nitrogen, 29% methane and 0.5% helium. A new deeper borehole at this site is planned to reach a depth of 10,000 m by the end of 1994.

To test Gold's hypothesis of abiogenic methane reserves in deep crystalline rock (Gold and Soter 1980; 1982), a deep borehole was sunk into a meteorite impact feature at Siljan where the induced fracturing was claimed to provide suitable reservoir properties in the crystalline rock. Results of that drilling, to over 5 km depth, have not been fully collated and published but claims of anomalous amounts of indigenous hydrocarbons tend not to be substantiated by available data: traces below 5 km have been linked to drilling lubricant contamination (Jeffrey and Kaplan, 1988). Methane was present in traces, particularly in association with dolerite intrusions (Jeffrey and Kaplan, 1988). $^3He/^4He$ data demonstrated that the deep helium was totally radiogenic with no detectable mantle-derived component (Hilton and Craig, 1987).

Deep wells in Kansas have been reported to contain up to 40 % hydrogen with total hydrocarbons only 1 %; the source of hydrogen is not clear and could be casing corrosion although deep serpentinisation and other mechanisms for reduction of water have also been suggested (Goebel et al., 1984; Coveney et al., 1987; Freund, 1984).

Low but significant quantities of hydrogen can often arise artificially from the corrosion of steel drill-pipe or borehole casing. The Permo-Trias brines in southern England were reported to have traces of hydrogen (less than or equal to 0.1 ml hydrogen per litre water, Darling, 1981), but it is not clear whether this was natural or artificial; the latter cause was given for similar traces of hydrogen in brines from the Jurassic Dogger aquifer deep in the Paris Basin

(Marty *et al.*, 1988). The reactions for the corrosion of steel in the ground are probably catalysed by microbes and can be represented by:

$$Fe + 2H_2O = Fe^{2+} + 2OH^- + H_2$$

$$3Fe + 4H_2O = Fe_3O_4 + 4H_2 .$$

In principle, in anaerobic sediments or soils, the hydrogen can be consumed by other bacteria to form methane, and the Fe(II) can be oxidised to Fe(III) with the further production of hydrogen e.g.

$$2Fe(OH)_2 = Fe_2O_3 + H_2O + H_2 .$$

In the absence of further iron corrosion, steady-state concentrations of hydrogen consistent with microbially controlled redox equilibria are established; these lie between less than 1.12×10^{-6} and 2.24×10^{-4} ml/l (Lovley and Goodwin, 1988).

B.9 METHANE IN DEEP FORMATION WATERS

Methane in formation waters may originate from the decarboxylation of acetic acid anions (Carothers and Kharaka, 1978). At temperatures of $80 - 200°C$, aliphatic acid anions are present in concentrations of up to about 5000 mg/l and may be the most abundant anions. Thermal degradation of these acids produces light organic gases (Carothers and Kharaka, 1978) according to reactions such as:

$$CH_3COO^- + H_2O = CH_4 + HCO_3^- .$$

Methane accounts for more than 90 % of the gas evolved. This methane is isotopically identical to thermogenic methane which evolves from thermal cracking of organic matter (Kharaka *et al.*, 1983).

Appendix C Theory of stable isotope use

The use of stable isotopes when studying microbial and inorganic chemical transformations is based on the fact that reactions distinguish between the stable isotopes of elements such as sulphur, carbon, oxygen, hydrogen and nitrogen. A chemical bond containing a lighter atom has a lower activation energy and therefore reacts more easily than the same bond involving a heavier atom. Microbes increase the rates of reactions by establishing pathways with lower activation energies. As reaction rates increase, so does the fractionation between heavy and light isotopes - the 'kinetic isotope effect'. Thus, for example, microbes will preferentially metabolise substrates containing the lighter isotope of the elements mentioned i.e. ^{32}S in preference to ^{34}S, ^{12}C in preference to ^{13}C, ^{16}O in preference to ^{18}O, ^{1}H in preference to ^{2}H (or deuterium, D) and ^{14}N in preference to ^{15}N (Ehrlich, 1981). Therefore, as a result of a chemical reaction that has involved microbial activity, the products will be enriched in the lighter isotope and the reactants enriched in the heavier isotope.

The enrichment in the lighter isotope in the product is compared either to the starting composition of the reactant, or to a reference standard that has not undergone any isotopic fractionation. All the work described here used the universal standards described by Faure (1986). The reference standard for sulphur is the S in troilite (FeS) of the iron meteorite Canyon Diablo. The reference standard for the carbon isotopes is the CO_2 gas obtained by reacting belemnites of the Peedee Formation (Cretaceous) of S. Carolina with 100% phosphoric acid — it is known as the PDB standard. The isotopic compositions of oxygen and hydrogen are reported in terms of differences of $^{16}O/^{18}O$ and $^{2}H/^{1}H$ ratios relative to a standard called SMOW (Standard Mean Ocean Water). The standard for nitrogen is the N_2 of the atmosphere. The accepted unit of isotopic ratio measurement is the delta value (δ), given in per mil ‰ units. The delta value is defined as:

$$\delta = \frac{(R_{sample} - R_{sample}).1000}{R_{standard}}$$

where R is the isotopic ratio of the element of interest.

Thus for carbon:

$$\delta^{13}C = \frac{\left[^{13}C/^{12}C_{sample} - {}^{13}C/^{12}C_{standard} \right].1000}{^{13}C/^{12}C_{standard}}$$

The delta value (δ) is thus a differential measure of the abundance of the heavier isotope. If δ is negative the sample is enriched in the light isotope relative to the reference standard; and if δ is positive it is enriched in the heavier isotope relative to the standard. The isotopic ratio of a sample is determined by mass spectrometry, allowing calculation of the isotopic fractionation. Isotopic fractionation is defined as the partitioning of isotopes of an element between two substances; as a result different isotope ratios are found in each substance. The main phenomena producing isotope fractionation are: isotope exchange reactions, kinetic processes (which mainly depend on the differences in reaction rates of isotopic molecules) and other physico-chemical effects such as evaporation, condensation, adsorption, desorption and diffusion.

A difficulty in the quantitative prediction of the stable isotope distribution among the components of a system is the experimental determination of the partitioning of the isotopes of a certain element amongst phases of geochemical interest over a wide range of temperatures.

To overcome this difficulty, isotopic fractionation factors can be calculated from theory (Bottinga, 1969). Isotopic fractionation between two materials, A and B, is described in terms of the fractionation factor α (A/B) where:

$$\alpha \ (A/B) = \frac{isotopic \ ratio \ of \ A}{istopic \ ratio \ of \ B}$$

e.g. for carbon isotopes in A and B:

$$\alpha \ (A/B) = \frac{\left[\delta^{13}C_{PDB}(A) - \delta^{13}C_{PDB}(B)\right]}{\left[\delta_{13}C_{PDB}(B) + 1000\right]} + 1$$

The process of methane oxidation has been extensively studied with the use of isotopes. Inorganic carbon has a typical $\delta13C$ value range from 0 to -5 ‰. Organic carbon in the form of plant material has an average $\delta13C$ value of about -27 ‰; the fractionation of carbon in plants is, however, variable, depending on the plant type e.g. a C3-type plant has a $\delta^{13}C$ value of around -30 ‰ but a C4-plant has a value of about -12 ‰ (Wright and Vanstone, 1991). Bacteriogenic methane has $\delta13C$ values ranging from -60 to -100 ‰, while thermogenic methane has $\delta^{13}C$ values from -20 to -60 ‰ (see Figure 44). During methane oxidation, isotopic fractionation occurs because it is a microbially mediated reaction with the microbes preferentially utilizing the lighter carbon isotope. Hence the residual methane becomes enriched in the heavier isotope while the product, carbon dioxide, becomes enriched in the lighter isotope. Stable carbon isotope studies, therefore, can be a sensitive indicator of methane oxidation.

BACTERIOGENIC SOURCES

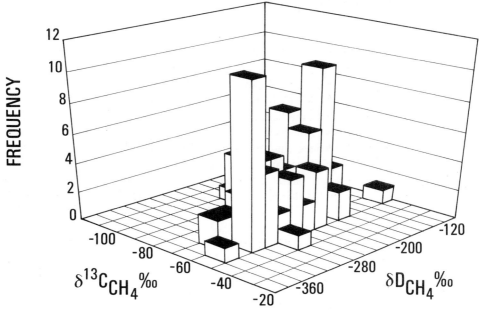

THERMOGENIC SOURCES

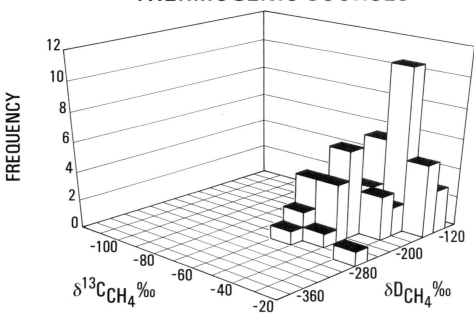

Figure 44 *Bacteriogenic and thermogenic methane: number frequency distribution of stable isotope ratios (after Hitchman et al., 1989)*

Appendix D Isotopic fractionation during aerobic methane oxidation

The process of aerobic methane oxidation has been shown to play a major role in stable isotope fractionation. In laboratory experiments the isotope separation factor between methane-containing gas and liquid phases was determined (Zyakun *et al.*, 1979, 1986). The experiment was performed both with and without methane-oxidising bacteria present in the system. When the bacteria were absent, it was found that the gaseous phase was initially enriched in ^{13}C due to the preferential diffusion of methane containing the lighter ^{12}C isotope from the gas into the liquid. However, this fractionation effect diminished with time since back-diffusion of methane from the gas phase into the liquid phase occurred, and the system achieved a dynamic equilibrium. When methane-oxidising bacteria were present in the liquid, back-diffusion of methane into the gas was prevented due to its complete consumption by the bacteria. The gas phase, therefore, became increasingly enriched in methane containing the heavier isotope as the experiment proceeded.

Isotopic studies of methane and carbon dioxide during experiments involving methane utilizing bacteria (Barker and Fritz, 1981b) showed that as methane oxidation progressed, the residual methane became enriched in ^{13}C relative to the starting methane, whereas the carbon dioxide produced during the oxidation became enriched in ^{12}C relative to the residual methane.

Laboratory experiments by Coleman *et al.* (1981) using cultures of methane oxidising bacteria, showed that the fractionation of both carbon and hydrogen isotopes increased as oxidation proceeded, with the residual methane becoming enriched in both ^{13}C and ^{2}H.

The findings of field observations (James and Burns, 1984; Barker and Fritz, 1981a) are similar to those of the methane oxidation experiments. The studies were of subsurface reservoir gas in offshore Australia, and groundwaters in Ontario, Canada. In both areas the process of aerobic methane oxidation was occurring and the residual methane was found to be enriched in ^{13}C.

Appendix E Isotopic fractionation during anaerobic methane oxidation

The effects of anaerobic methane oxidation have also been extensively studied with the aid of stable isotopes. In research on marine sediments deposited in anaerobic conditions with a moderately high addition rate of organic material (Alperin and Reeburgh, 1984), it was found that in the zone of methanogenesis, the carbon isotope ratios were typical of bacteriogenic methane, i.e. $\delta^{13}C$ more negative than -60 ‰. However, on rising toward the surface, the $\delta^{13}C$ values for the residual methane became less negative, or heavier in ^{13}C, while the values for carbon dioxide became more negative, or lighter (see Figure 45). Furthermore, Alperin *et al.* (1988) found that methane δ^2H and $\delta^{13}C$ depth profiles were similar in shape, i.e. both the methane hydrogen and carbon became preferentially enriched in the heavier isotopes as the sample depth decreased. It was concluded that anaerobic methane oxidation can significantly alter the hydrogen isotopic ratios as well as the carbon isotopic ratios in methane.

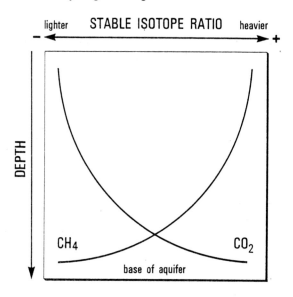

Figure 45 *Methane oxidation to carbon dioxide: hypothetical stable isotope ratio changes*

Artificial radionuclides, e.g. ^{14}C and ^{35}S, have been used to identify the occurrence of microbial sulphate reduction and anaerobic methane oxidation, as described by Coleman *et al.* (1981) and in detail by Reeburgh (1980). In a study of carbon isotopes in methane and carbon dioxide in sediment cores from Skan Bay, Aleutian Islands, it was found that the $\delta^{13}C$ profile for carbon dioxide was a mirror image of the $\delta^{12}C$ profile for methane, indicating that the two were connected (Reeburgh, 1980). The maximum rates of anaerobic methane oxidation and sulphate reduction both coincided with the depth interval over which methane, sulphate and carbon dioxide showed changes in concentration, suggesting that sulphate is the principal oxidant in the system. Rates of anaerobic methane oxidation were measured by injecting solutions of $^{14}CH_4$ and $Na_2{}^{35}SO_4$ into selected depth intervals of minimally disturbed sediment cores. After a period of time the carbon dioxide and hydrogen sulphide products were stripped from solution; the presence of $^{14}CO_2$ and $^{35}S^{2-}$ in these products was indicative that the processes of anaerobic methane oxidation and sulphate reduction were occurring simultaneously.

Appendix F Methane migration

F.1 GRAHAM'S LAW

The rate of diffusion of a gas is inversely proportion to the square root of its density (Graham's Law). Thus a light gas like methane (molecular weight 16) will migrate 1.65 times faster than a heavier gas such as carbon dioxide (molecular weight 44) according to the formula:

$$\frac{R_{CH_4}}{R_{CO_2}} = \sqrt{\frac{mol.wt.CO_2}{mol.wt.CH_4}} = \sqrt{\frac{44}{16}} = 1.65 \qquad \text{F.1}$$

F.2 MILLINGTON'S LAW

The simple equation of Millington is generally used to relate the diffusion coefficient of a gas in air to that in a porous medium (Baver *et al.*, 1972).

$$\frac{D}{D_o} = \phi^{1.33} \qquad \text{F.2}$$

where D is the effective diffusion coefficient in the porous medium, D_o is the diffusion coefficient in air and ϕ is the porosity of the medium. When the porous medium is filled with a liquid, the diffusion of the gas in the liquid can be treated in a similar way.

F.3 FICK'S LAWS

Fick's First Law of Diffusion for one-dimensional flow can be expressed as:

$$F = -D \cdot \frac{\partial C}{\partial x} \qquad \text{F.3}$$

where,
F = rate of transfer per unit area
C = concentration of the diffusing substance
x = distance normal to the cross-section along direction of flow
D = diffusion coefficient.

The general differential equation related to diffusion is known as Fick's Second Law of Diffusion and for one-dimensional flow is given by:

$$\frac{\partial C}{\partial t} = D \frac{\partial^2 C}{\partial x^2} \qquad \text{F.4}$$

For the case where initially the gas exists on one side of a plane interface normal to the x direction in the porous medium, the initial boundary conditions are:

$C = C_0$ at $x = 0$ and $t = 0$; and $C = 0$ where $x > 0$.

The solution is given by:

$$\frac{C}{C_o} = erfc\left(\frac{x}{2\sqrt{Dt}}\right)$$

F.5

where

C = the concentration of the gas at position x at time t
C_0 = the initial concentration of gas at $x = 0$, $t = 0$
t = the time from the start of diffusion.

The expression erfc( ) is the complementary error function which is obtainable from appropriate mathematical tables e.g. Crank (1979); Lerman (1979).

F.4 DARCY'S LAW

Viscous fluxes in porous media are generally described by Darcy's Law which relates fluid volume flux directly to pressure gradient and porous medium permeability (Lerman, 1979):

$$q = \frac{k}{\mu}\left(\frac{\Delta P}{L}\right)$$

F.6

where

q is the flux rate of the fluid, e.g. water or gas, across a unit cross sectional area
k is the permeability of the medium to the fluid
μ is the fluid viscosity
ΔP is the pressure difference over length L.

(See also Section F.6.1)

F.5 GAS LAYERING

In order to identify conditions in which methane layering may be a problem, use is made of a dimensionless quantity known as the Layering Number, L (Edwards, 1989), which is given by:

$$L = \frac{U}{\sqrt[3]{g\frac{d\rho}{\rho}\frac{q}{W}}}$$

F.7

where

U = ventilation velocity (m/s)
g = acceleration due to gravity (m/s^2)
$d\rho/\rho$ = relative density difference
q = the rate of input of the layer-forming gas (m^3/s)
W = width of the layer (m).

For the case of methane in air, the equation simplifies to:

$$L = \frac{1.63\ U}{\sqrt[3]{q/W}}$$

F.8

Layering can be controlled if air velocity is sufficient to maintain L at a value greater than 5 in a horizontal tunnel. The tendency for layering to form in a particular case will depend on the direction of airflow, gradient of the tunnel and the roughness of the walls.

F.6 GAS MIGRATION MODELLING PARAMETERS

F.6.1 Fluid flow and permeability

Darcy investigated the flow of water through sand filters. These investigations were confined to the flow of water through sand packs which were 100 % saturated with water. Later investigations found that Darcy's Law could be extended to other fluids as well as water. The generalised form of Darcy's Law is given in Equation F.6 and it can be re-written as follows:

$$v = \frac{k}{\mu} \cdot \left(\frac{\Delta P}{L}\right) \cdot \frac{1}{\phi} \qquad \text{F.9}$$

where
v = the velocity of flow (cm/s)
k = the permeability of the porous medium (Darcy)
ΔP = the pressure loss (dyne/cm^2)
μ = viscosity of the fluid (centipoise)
L = the average path length (cm)
ϕ = the volume fraction of the medium occupied by flowing fluid.

Fluid flow in circular tubes or conduits can been modelled by Poiseuille's equation for viscous flow:

$$v = \frac{d^2 \Delta P}{32 \mu L} \qquad \text{F.10}$$

and by Fanning's equation for turbulent flow:

$$v^2 = \frac{2d\Delta P}{f\rho L} \qquad \text{F.11}$$

where
v = fluid velocity (cm/s)
d = diameter of the conductor (cm)
ΔP = the pressure loss over length L (dyne/cm^2)
L = the length over which the pressure loss is measured (cm)
μ = fluid viscosity (centipoise)
ρ = fluid density (g/cm^3)
f = friction factor (dimensionless).

The use of Poiseuille's flow equation to define fluid flow in a porous medium assumes that a series of tubes of length L comprise the flow network. In real situations the flow network consist of a series of interconnected conduits of varying shapes and sizes. Since the pore structure of rocks does not permit simple classification, empirical data are required in most cases to calculate permeability.

Poiseuille's Law can be used in a form which is applicable to non-circular conduits by introducing the concept of mean hydraulic radius, m, where:

$$m = \frac{volume\ of\ conduit}{area\ of\ wetted\ surface} \qquad \text{F.12}$$

For a circular pipe:

$$m = \frac{\pi r^2 L}{2\pi r L} = \frac{d}{4} \qquad \text{F.13}$$

where r is the radius of the pipe. Substituting into Poiseuille's Law (Equation F.10) gives:

$$v = \frac{m^2 \Delta P}{2\mu L} \qquad\qquad \text{F.14}$$

Poiseuille's Law in this form is applicable to non-circular conduits. This expression was further developed by Wyllie $et\ al.$ (1952). He suggested that the factor 2 in the denominator of the above expression should be generalised and replaced by a shape factor k_o which takes values of between 2.5 and 3.0 to represent different porous materials. The factor m^2 can also be replaced by a combination of porosity, ϕ, tortuosity, τ, and the surface area per unit volume of pore space, S_p, (Amyx $et\ al.$, 1960) to give:

$$v = \frac{\phi}{k_o \tau^2 S_p^2} \cdot \frac{\Delta P}{\mu L} \qquad\qquad \text{F.15}$$

Equation F.15 with Darcy's Law offers a means of calculating k, the permeability of the porous medium.

F.6.2 Knudsen diffusion coefficients

Cummingham and Williams (1980) developed the following relationship for the determination of Knudsen diffusion coefficients assuming that the Klinkenberg effect and Knudsen diffusion are both dependent on the ratio of the mean molecular free path to the pore radius of a porous medium:

$$Dk_i = \frac{kb_i}{\mu_i} \qquad\qquad \text{F.16}$$

where
Dk_i is the Knudsen diffusion coefficient for gas component i
k is the permeability of the porous medium
b_i is the Klinkenberg parameter for gas component i
μ_i is the viscosity of gas component i.

Ghabaee and Rodwell (1989) concluded that the Klinkenberg factor of gas component i can be approximated by:

$$b_i = b_r \left(\frac{\mu_i}{\mu_r} \right) \left(\frac{M_r}{M_i} \right) \qquad\qquad \text{F.17}$$

where
M_i is the molecular weight of gas component i
M_r, μ_r and b_r are the molecular weight, viscosity and Klinkenberg factor respectively of the reference gas (for example air).

References

ABRAJANO, T.A., STURCHIO, N.C., BOHLKE, J.K., LYON, G.L., POREDA, R.J. AND STEVENS, C.M. (1988)
Methane-hydrogen gas seeps, Zambales Ophiolite Philippines: deep or shallow origin?
Origins of Methane in the Earth (Guest Ed. M. Scheoll)
Chemical Geology, 71, pp211-222

ALEXANDER, M. (1985)
Biodegradation of organic chemicals
Environmental Science and Technology, 18, pp106-111.

ALPERIN, M.J. AND REEBURGH, W.S. (1984)
Geochemical observations supporting anaerobic methane oxidation
In: *Microbial Growth on C1 Compounds* (Eds. R.L. Crawford and R.S. Hanson)
American Society for Microbiology, pp282-289.

ALPERIN, M.J., REEBURGH, W.S. AND WHITICAR, M.J. (1988)
Carbon and hydrogen isotope fractionation resulting from anaerobic methane oxidation
Global and Biogeochemical Cycles, 2, pp279-288.

AMYX, J.W., BASS, D.M. AND WHITING, R.L. (1960)
Petroleum Reservoir Engineering, Physical Properties
McGraw-Hill Book Co.

ANDERSON, I. (1987)
Nyos: the danger may not be over
New Scientist, 5 February, pp30-31.

ANDREWS, J.N. (1987)
Noble gases in groundwaters from crystalline rocks
In: *Saline Water and Gases in Crystalline Rocks* (Eds. P. Fritz and S. Frape), Geological Association of Canada Special Paper 33, pp234-244.

ANDREWS, J.N., BALDERER, W., BATH, A.H., CLAUSEN, H.B., EVANS, G.V., FLORKOWSKI, T., GOLDBRUNNER, J., IVANOVICH, M., LOOSLI, H. AND ZOJER, H. (1984)
Environmental isotope studies in two aquifer systems: a comparison of groundwater dating methods. *Isotope Hydrology 1983, Proc. Int. Symp. on Isotope Hydrology in Water Resources Development*
IAEA, Vienna, pp535-576.

ANDREWS, J.N. AND WILSON, G.B. (1987)
The composition of dissolved gases in deep groundwaters and groundwater degassing
In: *Saline Water and Gases in Crystalline Rocks*, (Eds. P. Fritz and S. Frape), Geological Association of Canada Special Paper 33, 245–252.

ANDREWS, J.N., HUSSAIN, N. AND YOUNGMAN, M.J. (1989)
Atmospheric and radiogenic gases in groundwaters from the Stripa granite
Geochimica et Cosmochimica Acta, 53, pp1831-1841.

ARNÓRSSON, S. AND GUNNLAUGSSON, E. (1985)
New gas geothermometers for geothermal exploration-calibration and application
Geochimica et Cosmochimica Acta, 49, pp1307-1325.

BAKER, B. (1989)
Survey of current practice for building on contaminated land
DoE report for DoE research contract PECD 7/10/235

BARBER, C., DAVIS, G.B., BRIEGEL, D. AND WARD, J.K. (1990)
Factors controlling the concentration of methane and other volatiles in groundwater and soil gas around a waste site
Journal of Contaminant Hydrology, 5, pp155-169.

BARKER, C. (1987)
Development of abnormal and subnormal pressures in reservoirs containing bacterially generated gas
Bulletin of the American Association of Petroleum Geologists, 71, pp1404-1413.

BARKER, J.F. AND FRITZ, P. (1981A)
The occurrence and origin of methane in some groundwater flow systems
Canadian Journal of Earth Science, 18, pp1802-1816

BARKER, J.F. AND FRITZ, P. (1981B)
Carbon isotope fractionation during microbial methane oxidation
Nature, 293, pp289-291

BARNARD, P.C. AND COOPER, B.S. (1983)
A review of geochemical data related to the northwest European gas province
In: *Petroleum Geochemistry and Exploration of Europe*
Geol. Soc. (London) Spec. Publ., pp19-33

BARNES, I. (1984)
Volatiles of Mount Saint Helens and their origins
Journal of Volcanology and Geothermal Research, 22, pp133-146

BARRY, D.L. (1986)
Hazards from methane on contaminated sites
Proceedings of the International Conference on Building on Marginal and Derelict Land, Glasgow, 7-9 May, pp209-224

BARRY, D.L. (1987)
Hazards from methane and carbon dioxide
In: *Reclaiming Contaminated Land* (Ed. T. Cairney)
Blackie & Son Ltd., Glasgow and London

BARRY, D.L. AND RAYBOULD, J.G. (1988)
Landfill gas migration hazards
Paper in the Proceedings of the Second International Conference on Construction in Areas of Abandoned Mineworkings, Edinburgh, 28-30 June

BATH, A.H., EDMUNDS, W.M. AND ANDREWS, J.N. (1979)
Palaeoclimatic trends deduced from the hydrochemistry of a Triassic Sandstone aquifer
UK Isotope Hydrology 1978, Proc. Symp. Vienna II, IAEA, Vienna, pp545-568

BATH, A.H., BRASSELL, S.C., EGLINTON, G., HILL, R.I., HOOKER, P.J., O'NIONS, R.K.O., OXBURGH, E.R., PARNELL, J., ROBINSON, N. AND SPIRO, B. (1986)
Deep source gases and hydrocarbons in the UK crust
Rep. Brit. Geol. Surv. FLPU 86−2

BATH, A.H., DARLING, W.G., HITCHMAN, S.P., ANDREWS, J.N., CAVE, M.R., GREEN K.A. AND REEDER, S. (1988)
Chemical and stable isotopic analyses of dissolved gases and groundwater seepages collected from Wyresdale Tunnel, November 1987
Tech. Rep. Brit. Geol. Surv. Fluid Processes Group WE/88/1C

BATH, A.H. AND FALCK, W.E. (1991)
Sources, abundances and reactions of gases in the repository far-field
Tech. Rep. Brit. Geol. Surv. Fluid Processes Group WE/90/32

BAVER, L.D., GARDNER, W.H. AND GARDNER, W.R. (1972)
Soil Physics
Wiley, New York.(4th Edition)

BEAR, J. (1972)
Dynamics of Fluids in Porous Media
Elsevier Scientific Publishers, New York

BEEBE, R.R. and RAUCH, H.W. (1979)
Lineaments and groundwater chemistry as exploration tools for Devonian shale gas in the Midway-Extra field of West Virginia
In: *Proceedings of the Third Eastern Gas Shales Symposium* (Ed. H. Barlow)
U.S.D.O.E.

BERESFORD, J.J. (1989)
Permanent works design
Paper 4.2, Methane — Facing the Problems
Symposium, Nottingham, 26-28 September

BERG, R.R. (1986)
Review of Sandstones
Prentice Hall, Englewood Cliffs

BGS (1984)
Isotopic and chemical analyses of gas and associated water - Wyresdale Tunnel
Stable Isotope Rep. Brit. Geol. Surv. No. 108
(Authors: B. Spiro, M. Miller and A.H. Bath). Unpublished report to Health & Safety Executive

BGS (1985)
Abbeystead: Geological context of the Wyresdale Tunnel methane explosion
Tech. Rep. Brit. Geol. Surv. WA/89/30
(Authors: A. Wilson, A. Brandon and E.W. Johnson. Unpublished report to NWWA.)

BGS (1985)
Wyresdale Tunnel investigations: notes on hydrochemistry
(Authors: A.H. Bath, M.R. Cave and W.G. Darling. Unpublished report to NWWA.)

BGS (1988)
Chemical and stable isotopic analyses of dissolved gases and groundwater seepages collected from Tunnel, November 1987.
Tech. Rep. Brit. Geol. Surv. WE/88/1C
(Authors: A.H. Bath, W.G. Darling, S.P. Hitchman, J.N. Andrews, M.R. Cave, K.A. Green and S. Reeder. Unpublished report to NWWA.)

BISHOP, W.D., CARTER, R.C., AND LUDWIG, H.F. (1966)
Water pollution hazards from refuse produced carbon dioxide
The Third International Conference on Water Pollution Research, Section 1 Paper 10
Water Pollution Control Federation, Washington D.C.

BOLT, G.H. AND BRUGGENWERT, M.G.M. (1976)
Soil Chemistry, A. Basic Elements, Developments in Soil Science 5A
Elsevier, Oxford

BOTTINGA, Y. (1969)
Fractionation factors for carbon and hydrogen isotope exchange in the system calcite-carbon
dioxide-graphite-methane-hydrogen-water vapor
Geochimica et Cosmochimica Acta, 33, pp49-64

BOWEN, R. (1988)
Isotopes in the Earth Sciences
Elsevier, London and New York

BROOKES, B.I. AND YOUNG, P.J. (1983)
The development of sampling and gas chromotography-mass spectometry analytical procedures
to identify and determine the minor organic components of landfill gas
Talanta, 30, pp665-676

BUILDING RESEARCH ESTABLISHMENT (1977)
Ventilation Requirements
Building Research Establishment Digest, 206
HMSO, London

BURKE, K. (1963)
Dissolved gases in the East African Rift lakes
Nature, 198, pp568-569

BUTTERWORTH, J.S. (1991)
Methane, carbon dioxide and the development of contaminated sites
Paper 2.4, Methane – Facing the Problems
Symposium, Nottingham, 26-28 March

CAROTHERS, W.W. AND KHARAKA, Y.K. (1978)
Aliphatic acid anions in oil-field waters-implications for the origins of natural gas
Bulletin of the American Association of Petroleum Geologists, 62, pp2441-2453

CARTER, R.A. (1991)
Methane fever flares in USA
Engineering and Mining Journal, February, 16C-16G

CHAMP, D.R., GULENS, J. AND JACKSON, R.E. (1979)
Oxidation reduction sequences in groundwater flow systems
Canadian Journal of Earth Sciences, 16, pp12-23

CHANTON, J.P., PAULY, G.G., MARTENS, C.S., BLAIR, N.E., AND DACEY, J.W.H.
(1988)
Carbon isotopic composition of methane in Florida Everglades soils and fractionation during its
transport to the troposphere
Global Biogeochemical Cycles, 2, pp245-252

CICERONE, R.J. AND OREMLAND, R.S. (1988)
Biogeochemical aspects of atmospheric methane
Global Biogeochemical Cycles, 2, pp299-327

CLAYPOOL, G.E. AND KAPLAN, I.R. (1974)
In: *The Origin and Distribution of Methane in Marine Sediments* I.R. Kaplan (Ed.)
Plenum Press, pp99

CLAYPOOL, G.E. AND KVENVOLDEN, K.A. (1983)
Methane and other hydrocarbon gases in marine sediment
Ann. Rev. Earth Planet. Sci., 11, pp299-327

COLEMAN, D.D., RISATTI, J.B. AND SCHOELL, M. (1981)
Fractionation of carbon and hydrogen isotopes by methane-oxidising bacteria
Geochimica et Cosmochimica Acta, 45, pp1033-1037

COLEMAN, D.D., LIU, E.L. AND RILEY, K.M. (1988)
Microbial methane in the shallow Paleozoic sediments and glacial deposits of Illinois, USA
Chemical Geology, 71, pp23-40

COLT, J.E. (1983)
The computation and reporting of dissolved gas levels
Water Research, Vol. 17, No. 4, pp841-849

COVENEY, R.M., GOEBEL, E.D., ZELLER, E.J., DRESCHOFF, G.A.M.
AND ANGINO, E.E. (1987)
Serpentinization and the origin of hydrogen gas in Kansas
Bulletin of the American Association of Petroleum Geologists, 71, pp39-48

CRAIG, H. AND LUPTON, J.E. (1981)
Helium-3 and mantle volatiles in the ocean and the ocean crust
In: *The Sea*, Vol. 7, The Oceanic Lithosphere (Ed. C. Emiliani)
John Wiley & Sons, pp391-428

CRANK, J. (1979)
The Mathematics of Diffusion
Clarendon, Oxford

CREEDY, D.P. (1989)
Geological sources of methane in relation to surface and underground hazards
Paper 1.4 Methane − Facing the Problems
Symposium, Nottingham, 26-28 September

CREEDY, D.P. (1991A)
Methane in coal mines − threats and opportunities
Paper 1.2 Methane − Facing the Problems
Symposium, Nottingham, 26-28 March

CREEDY, D.P. (1991B)
An introduction to geological aspects of methane occurrence and control in British deep coal mines
Quarterly Journal of Engineering Geology, 24, pp209-220

CRILL, P.M., BARTLETT, K.B., HARRISS, R.C., GORHAM, E., VERRY, E.S.,
SEBACHER, D.I., MADZAR, L. AND SANNER, W. (1988)
Methane flux from Minnesota peatlands
Global Biogeochemical Cycles, 2, pp371-384

CRONER (1991)
Substances Hazardous to Health
Croner Publications Ltd., Surrey

CROWHURST, D. and MANCHESTER, S.J. (1993)
The measurement of methane and other gases from the ground
Report 131, CIRIA, London

CUMMINGHAM, R.E. AND WILLIAMS, R.J.J. (1980)
Diffusion in Gases and Porous Media
Plenum Press, New York

DARLING, W.G. (1981)
The analysis of free and dissolved gases by chromatography
Tech. Rep. Brit. Geol. Surv. Hydrogeology Series WD/ST/81/9

DARLING, W.G. (1985)
Methane in the chalk groundwater of central London
Tech. Rept. Brit. Geol. Surv. Hydrogeology Series WD/ST/85/3

DARLING, W.G. AND BATH, A.H. (1986)
Methane concentrations in some scottish hydro-electric tunnels
Tech. Rep. Brit. Geol. Surv. Hydrogeology Series WD/ST/86/7

DEPARTMENT OF THE ENVIRONMENT (1986)
Landfilling Wastes
Waste Management Paper No. 26
HMSO, London

DEPARTMENT OF THE ENVIRONMENT (1989)
The Control of Landfill Gas
Waste Management Paper No. 27
HMSO, London

DES MARAIS, D.J. AND TRUESDELL, A.H. (1987)
Methane and higher hydrocarbons in hydrothermal environments of western North America
Geological Society of America Abstracts Program, 19, p641

DEVOL, A.H. (1983)
Methane oxidation rates in the anaerobic sediments of Saahnich Inlet
Limnology and Oceanography, 28, pp738-742

DEVOL, A.H. AND AHMED, S. (1981)
Are high rates of sulphate reduction associated with anaerobic oxidation of methane?
Nature, 291, pp407-408

DILLON, W.P. AND PAULL, C.K. (1983)
Marine gas hydrates, 2, Geophysical evidence
In: *Natural Gas Hydrates: Properties, Occurrences and Recovery* (Ed. J.L. Cox)
Butterworth Publishers, Boston, pp73-90

DOELLE, H.W. (1975)
Bacterial Metabolism
Academic Press, London

DRUMMOND, S.E.J. (1981)
Boiling and Mixing of Hydrothermal Fluids: Chemical Effects on Mineral Precipitation.
Unpublished PhD Thesis, Pennsylvania State University

DYCK, W., CHATTERJEE, A.K., GEMMELL, D.E. AND MURRICANE, K. (1976)
Well water trace element reconnaissance, eastern maritime Canada
Journal of Geochemical Exploration, 6, pp139-162

EBBERN, J. (1981)
The geology of the Morecambe gas field
In: *Petroleum Geology of the Continental Shelf of North-West Europe*
Institute of Petroleum, London, pp485-493

ECL (1986)
Final Geological / Geophysical Report Lancashire Conjunctive Use Scheme; Further Investigations: Wyresdale Tunnel
(Authors: S.R. Lawrence, P.W. Coster and D.J. Taylor. Unpublished report to NWWA.)

ECL (1988)
An analysis of methane ingress data for the Wyresdale Tunnel − Final Report
(Author: P.W. Coster. Unpublished report to NWWA.)

EDWARDS, J.S. 1989
Gases - their basic properties
Paper 1.3 Methane − Facing the Problems
Symposium, Nottingham, 26-28 September

EDWARDS, J.S. (1991)
Methane in groundwater
Paper 2.3 Methane − Facing the Problems
Symposium, Nottingham, 26-28 March

EHRLICH, H.L. (1981)
Geomicrobiology
Marcel Dekker Inc., New York

ELLIOT T., TOMLINSON, M.J., FOXFORD, K.A., HOLBROUGH, D.J., AND SEARLE, D.M. (1989)
Migration of gases through fractured argillaceous rocks: experimental work at the Reskajeage Farm quarry site, Cornwall
Nirex Safety Studies Report No. NSS/R147, UK Nirex Ltd

EMBERTON, J.R. (1984)
Gas composition tables
AERE Report M-3432

ETSU (1988)
A basic study of landfill microbiology
ETSU B 1159
Energy Technology Support Unit, Harwell

FAURE, G. (1986)
Principles of Isotope Geology (2nd Edition)
John Wiley and Sons

FERGUSON, J. (1984)
The methane content of some Carboniferous limestones from the northern Pennines and its relationship to mineralisation
Proceedings of the Yorkshire Geological Society, 45, pp67-69

FERNANDEZ, I.J. AND KOSIAN, P.A. (1987)
Soil-air carbon dioxide concentrations in a New England spruce-fir forest
Journal of the Soil Science Society of America, 51, pp261-263

FINDIKAKIS, A.N. AND LECKIE, J.O. (1979)
Numerical simulation of gas flow in sanitary landfills
Journal of Environmental Engineering Div., Proceedings of the American Society of Civil Engineers, Vol. 105, No. EE5

FOWLER, D. (1991)
Methane restricts clayboard use
New Civil Engineer, April, p5

FREUND, F. (1984)
H2 and N2 gas from magmatic rocks − a solid state viewpoint
Oil and Gas Journal, 20 August

FRITZ, P., FRAPE, S.K. AND MILES, M. (1987)
Methane in the crystalline rocks of the Canadian Shield
In: *Saline Water and Gases in Crystalline Rocks* (Eds. P. Fritz and S.K. Frape) Geological
Association of Canada Special Paper, 33, pp211-223

GAMES, L.M. AND HAYES, J.M. (1976)
On the mechanisms of CO2 and CH4 production in natural anaerobic environments
In: *Environmental Biogeochemistry* (Ed. O. Jerome)
Ann Arbor Science

GAUTSCHI, A., FABER, E., MEYER, J., MULLIS, J., SCHENKER, F. AND
BALLENTINE, C. (1990)
Hydrocarbon and noble gases in fluid inclusions of Alpine calcite veins − implications for
hydrocarbon exploration
Bulletin of the Swiss Assoc. of Petroleum Geology and Engineering, Vol. 56, No. 131, pp13-36

GEOLOGICAL SURVEY OF GREAT BRITAIN (1963)
Summary of Progress for 1962
HMSO, London

GERLACH, T.M. (1980A)
Evaluation of volcanic gases from Kilauea volcano
Journal of Volcanology and Geothermal Research, 7, pp295-317

GERLACH, T.M. (1980B)
Chemical characteristics of the volcanic gases from Nyirongo lava lake and the generation of
CH4-rich fluid inclusions in alkaline rocks
Journal of Volcanology and Geothermal Research, 8, pp177-189

GERLACH, T.M. AND NORDLIE, B.E. (1975)
The C-H-O-S gaseous system, Part II: Tempertaure, atomic composition and molecular
equilibria in volcanic gases
American Journal of Science, 275, pp377-394

GHABAEE, K. AND RODWELL W.R. (1989)
Landfill gas modelling, a literature survey of landfill gas generation and migration
Atomic Energy Authority Report No. R2567, Petroleum Reservoir Technology Division, AEA
Winfrith

GIGGENBACH, W.F., GARCIA, N., LONDONO, P.A, RODRIGUEZ, V., ROJAS, N.
AND CALVACHE, M.L. (1990)
The chemistry of fumarolic vapor and thermal-spring discharges from the Nevado del Ruiz
volcano-magmatic-hydrothermal system
Colombia Journal of Volcanology and Geothermal Research, 42, pp13-39

GODOY, F.E. AND NALEID, D.S. (1990)
Optimizing the use of soil gas surveys
Hazardous Materials Control, Vol. 3, No. 5, pp23-29

GOEBEL, E.D., COVENEY, R.M., ANGINO, E.E., ZELLER, E.J. AND
DRESCHOFF, G.A.M. (1984)
Geology, composition, isotopes of naturally occurring H_2/N_2 rich gas from wells near Junction
City, Kansas
Oil and Gas Journal, 7 May, pp215-222

GOLD T. AND SOTER, S. (1980)
The deep-earth gas hypothesis
Scientific American, 242, pp130-137

GOLD T. AND SOTER, S. (1982)
Abiogenic methane and the origin of petroleum
Energy Exploration and Exploitation, 1, pp89-104

GRANT, W.D. AND LONG, P.E. (1981)
Environmental Microbiology
Blackie & Son Ltd

GUNSALUS, R.P., ZEIKUS, J.G. AND WOLFE, R.S. (1972)
Microbial modification of groundwaters
Research Report No. 57, University of Illinios Water Resources Centre

HALCROW (1989)
Abbeystead Outfall Works − Repairs and Modifications. Report on Investigations in Wyresdale Tunnel (Volumes 1 and 2)
(Author: Sir William Halcrow and Partners. Unpublished report to NWWA).

HARRISS, R.C., SEBACHER, D.I., BARTLETT, K.B., BARTLETT, D.S., AND CRILL, P.M. (1988)
Sources of atmospheric methane in the South Florida environment
Global Biogeochemical Cycles, 2, pp231-243

HEALD, E.F., NAUGHTON, J.J. AND BARNES, I.L. (1963)
The chemistry of volcanic gases: 2, Use of equilibrium calculations in the interpretation of volcanic gas samples
Journal of Geophysical Research, 68, pp545-557

HEALTH & SAFETY EXECUTIVE (1985)
The Abbeystead explosion − A report of the investigation by the Health & Safety Executive into the explosion on 23 May 1984 at the valve house of the Lune/Wyre water transfer scheme at Abbeystead
HMSO, London

HEATON, T.H.E. AND VOGEL, J.C. (1981)
'Excess air' in groundwater
Journal of Hydrology, 50, pp201-216

HENLEY, R.W., TRUESDELL, A.H. AND BARTON, P.B. (1984)
Fluid-mineral equilibria in hydrothermal systems
Reviews in Economic Geology, Vol 1.
Society of Economic Geologists, Texas, USA

HILTON, D.R. AND CRAIG, H. (1987)
The Siljan deep well: helium isotope results
Abstract, Eos, Transactions of the American Geophysical Union, 68, p1514

HITCHMAN, S.P., DARLING, W.G. AND WILLIAMS, G.M. (1989)
Stable isotope ratios in methane containing gases in the United Kingdom
Tech. Rep. Brit. Geol. Surv. WE/89/30

HOVLAND, M. AND JUDD, A.G. (1988)
Seabed Pockmarks and Seepages
Graham and Trotman, London

HUDSON, J.A. (1989)
Rock Mechanics Principles in Engineering Practice
CIRIA Report, Butterworths

INITIAL REPORTS OF THE DEEP SEA DRILLING PROGRAM, LEG 64, (1982)
Mazatlan, Mexico to Long Beach, California, sites 474-480, 211-416.

IRWIN, W.P. AND BARNES, I. (1980)
Tectonic relations of carbon dioxide discharges and earthquakes
Journal of Geophysical Research, 85(B6), pp3115-3121

IVERSEN, N. AND JØRGENSEN, B.B. (1985)
Anaerobic methane oxidation rates at the sulphate-methane transition in marine sediments from
Kattegat and Skagerrak (Denmark)
Limnology and Oceanography, 30, pp944-955

JAITLY, P. (1977)
Methane contamination − synopsis of current information and practice
London Environmental Supplements Report of the Docklands Joint Committee Working Group
on Methane
Pollution Monitoring Group, GLC Scientific Services Branch, County Hall, London

JAMES, A.T. AND BURNS, B.J. (1984)
Microbial alteration of subsurface natural gas accumulations
Bulletin of the American Association of Petroleum Geologists, 68, pp957-960

JEFFREY, A.W.A. AND KAPLAN, I.R. (1988)
Hydrocarbons and inorganic gases in the Gravberg-1 well, Siljan Ring, Sweden
In: *Origins of Methane in the Earth* (Guest Ed. M. Schoell)
Chemical Geology, 71, pp 237-255

JENDEN P.D. AND KAPLAN, I.R. (1986)
Comparison of microbial gases from the Middle America Trench and Scripps Submarine
Canyon: implications for the origin of natural gas
Applied Geochemistry, 1, pp631-646

JENDEN, P.D. AND KAPLAN, I.R. (1989)
Origin of natural gas in the Sacramento Basin, California
Bulletin of the American Association of Petroleum Geologists, 73, pp431-453

JOHNSON, E.W. (1981)
A tunnel section through a prograding Namurian (Arnsbergian, E2a) delta, in the western
Bowland Fells, north Lancashire
Geological Journal, 16, pp93-110

JONES, D.S. AND RAUCH, H.W. (1978)
Lineaments and groundwater quality as exploration tools for groundwater and gas in the
Cottageville area of western West Virginia
Proceedings of the Second Eastern Gas Shales Symposium,
U.S.D.O.E.

KANOL, D.W. AND ZETTHER, G.H. (1990)
In: *Proceedings of the 5th Sewage and Refuse Symposium*
Abwassertechnische Vereinnigung ev., Munich, 198, pp859-870

KAPLAN, I.R. (Ed.) (1974)
Natural Gases in Marine Sediments
Plenum Press, New York and London

KARIMI, A., RAVIDRAN, V., AND PIRBAZARI, M. (1988)
A laboratory experiment and predictive model for evaluating landfill cover controls of emission of volatile organic chemicals to air
Waste and Hazardous Material, 3, pp203-218

KAWABE, I., MAKI, T. AND SUGISAKI, R. (1981)
Geochemical study on subsurface gases in the fault zones of Shikoku Island, Japan-I: Bubble gas survey around the Median Tectonic Line
Geochemical Journal, 15, pp183-191

KELLY, W.R., MATISOFF, G. AND FISHER, J.B. (1985)
The effects of a gas well blow out on groundwater chemistry
Environmental Geology Water Science, 7, pp205-213

KHARAKA, Y.K., CAROTHERS, W.M. AND ROSENBAUER, R.J. (1983)
Thermal decarboxylation of acetic acid: implications for the origins of natural gas
Geochimica et Cosmochimica Acta, 47, pp397-402

KOZLOVSKY, Y.A. (1984)
The world's deepest well
Scientific American, 251, pp98-104

KROOSS, B.M., LEYTHAEUSER, D. AND SCHAEFER, R.G. (1988)
Light hydrocarbon diffusion in a caprock
In: *Origins of Methane in the Earth* (Guest Ed. M. Schoell)
Chemical Geology, 71, pp65-76

KVENVOLDEN K.A. AND SIMONEIT, B.R.T. (1990)
Hydrothermally derived petroleum from Guaymas Basin, Gulf of California, and Escabana Trough, Northeast Pacific ocean
Bulletin of the American Association of Petroleum Geologists, 74, pp223-237

KVENVOLDEN, K.A. (1988)
Methane hydrate - a major reservoir of carbon in the shallow geosphere?
In: *Origins of Methane in the Earth* (Guest Ed. M. Schoell)
Chemical Geology, 71, pp41-51

LAMONT, D. (1989)
Safety and BS6164
Paper 1.1 Methane − Facing the Problems
Symposium, Nottingham, 26-28 September

LARGE, P.J. (1983)
Methylotrophy and Methanogenesis, Aspects of Microbiology, 8
Van Nostrand Reinhold, UK

LAWRENCE, S.R., COSTER, P.W. AND IRELAND, R.J. (1987)
Structural development and petroleum potential of the northern flanks of the Bowland Basin (Carboniferous), North-west England
In: *Petroleum Geology of North West Europe* (Eds. J. Brooks and K. Glennie)
Graham and Trotman, pp225-233

LAWSON, P. AND ALSTON, Y.R. (Eds.) (1989)
Proceedings of Landfill Microbiology: R & D Workshop, Harwell, United Kingdom
Department of the Environment

LEACH, B.A. AND GOODGER, H.K. (1991)
Building on derelict land
CIRIA Special Publication SP78
CIRIA, London

LERMAN, A. (1979)
Geochemical Processes
John Wiley and Sons, Inc.

LOVLEY, D.R. AND GOODWIN, S. (1988)
Hydrogen concentrations as an indicator of the predominant terminal electron-accepting
reactions in aquatic sediments
Geochimica et Cosmochimica Acta, 52, pp2993-3003

LYON, G.L., GIGGENBACH, W.F. AND LUPTON, J.E. (1990)
Composition and origin of the hydrogen-rich gas seep, Fiordland, New Zealand
Eos, Transactions of the American Geophysical Union, Vol. 71, No. 43, p1717

MACDONALD, G.J. (1983)
The many origins of natural gas
Journal of Petroleum Geology, Vol. 5, No. 4, pp341-362

MARRERO, T.R. AND MASSON, E.A. (1972)
Gaseous diffusion coefficients
Journal of Physical and Chemical Reference Data, 1, pp3-118

MARTENS, C.S. AND BERNER, R.A. (1977)
Interstitial water chemistry of anoxic Long Island Sound sediments
Limnology and Oceanography, 22, pp1419-1420

MARTY, B., CRIAUD, A. AND FOUILLAC, C. (1988)
Low enthalpy geothermal fluids from the Paris sedimentary basin - 1
Characteristics and origin of gases
Geothermics, 17, pp619-633

MASON, E.A. AND MALINAUSKAS A.P. (1983)
Gas Transport in Porous Media: The Dusty Gas Model
Chemical Engineering Monographs, 194
Elsevier, New York

MATTHESS, G. (1982)
The Properties of Groundwater
John Wiley and Sons, Chichester

MAZOR, E. (1972)
Paleotemperatures and other hydrological parameters deduced from noble gases dissolved in
groundwaters: Jordan Rift Valley, Israel
Geochimica et Cosmochimica Acta, 36, pp1321-1336

MOGILEVSKY, G.A. (1964)
Changes in the composition of hydrocarbon gases under the action of bacteria as evidence of
gas migration
In: *Advances in Organic Geochemistry* (Eds. U. Columbo and G.D. Hobson)
Pergamon Press, pp359-360

MOORE, C.A. (1979)
Landfill gas migration and controls
CRC Critical Review of Environmental Control, 2, pp157-183

MOORE W.J. (1981)
Physical Chemistry
Longman Group Ltd.

MUIR WOOD, A.M. (1975)
Tunnel Hazards: UK experience.
Hazards in tunnelling and on falsework
Institute of Civil Engineering, pp. 47-59.

MULLIS, J. (1987)
Organic matter in low-grade metamorphism
In: *Low Temperature Metamorphism* (Ed. M. Frey)
Blackie, London

NADEN, J. AND SHEPHERD, T.J. (1989)
Role of methane and carbon dioxide in gold deposition
Nature, 12, pp793-795

NAUGHTON, J.J., EMERSON, F.H. AND BARNES, I.L. (1963)
The chemistry of volcanic gases: 1. Collection and analysis of equilibrium mixtures by gas chromatography
Journal of Geophysical Research, 68, pp539-557

NEAL, C. AND STANGER, G. (1983)
Hydrogen generation from mantle source rocks in Oman
Earth and Planetary Science Letters, 66, pp315-320

NEHRING, N.L. AND AMORE, F.D. (1984)
Gas chemistry and thermometry of the Cerro Prieto, Mexico, geothermal field
Geothermics, 13, pp75-89

NEHRING, N.L. AND FAUSTO, J.J. (1979)
Gases in steam from Cerro Prieto geothermal wells with a discussion of steam/gas ratio measurements.
Geothermics, 8, pp253-255

OREMLAND, R.S. AND TAYLOR, B.F. (1978)
Sulphate reduction and methanogenesis in marine sediments
Geochimica et Cosmochimica Acta, 42, pp209-214

OREMLAND, R.S., MILLER, L.G. AND WHITICAR, M.J. (1987)
Sources and flux of natural gases from Mono Lake, California
Geochimica et Cosmochimica Acta, 51, pp2915-2929

ORR, W.E., MUIR WOOD, SIR A., BEAVER, J.L., IRELAND, R.J. AND BEAGLEY, D.P. (1991)
Abbeystead outfall works: background to repairs and modifications − and lessons learnt.
Journal of the Institution of Water and Environmental Management, 5, pp7-20

OSKARSSON, N. (1990)
Carbon dioxide bursts of Lake Nyos, Cameroon, modelled as periodic supersaturation in a countercurrent reactor
Journal of Volcanology and Geothermal Research, 42, pp307-318

PANDEY, G.N., TECK, M.R. AND KATZ, D.L. (1974)
Diffusion of fluids through porous media with implications in engineering geology
Bulletin of the American Association of Petroleum Geologists, 21, pp291-303

PANGANIBAN, A.T., JNR., PATT, T.E., HART, W. AND HANSON, R.S. (1979)
Oxidation of methane in the absence of oxygen in lake water samples
Applied and Environmental Microbiology, 37, pp303-309

PEARSON, C.F.C. (1989)
Construction aspects
Paper 4.1 Methane − Facing the Problems
Symposium, Nottingham, 26-28 September

PEARSON, C.F.C. (1991)
Methane occurrence, detection and monitoring during the construction and operation of underground civil engineering projects
Paper 1.5 Methane − Facing the Problems
Symposium, Nottingham, 26-28 March

PEARSON, C.F.C. AND BROWN, M.J. (1990)
A case study of biofilm formation in association with methane seepage into an underground tunnel
In: *Microbiology in Civil Engineering* (Ed. P. Howsam)
Proc. FEMS Symposium No.59, E. & F.N. Spon, pp328-340

PEARSON, F. AND EDWARDS, J.S. (1989)
Methane entry into the Carsington Aqueduct system
Paper 4.3 Methane − Facing the Problems
Symposium, Nottingham, 26-28 September

PETERSIL'YE, I.A. AND PRIPACHKIN, V.A. (1979)
Hydrogen, carbon, nitrogen and helium in gases from igneous rocks
Geochemistry International, Vol. 16, No. 4, pp50-55

PINEAU, F., JAVOY, M. AND BOTTINGA, Y. (1976)
$^{13}C/^{12}C$ ratios of rocks and inclusions in popping rocks of the Mid-Atlantic Ridge
Earth and Planetary Science Letters, 29, pp413-421

PYE, K. AND MILLER, J.A. (1990)
Chemical and biochemical weathering of pyritic mudrocks in a shale embankment
Quarterly Journal of Engineering Geology, 23, pp365-381

QUAY, P.D., KING, S.L., LANSDOWN, J.M. AND WILBUR, D.O. (1988)
Isotopic composition of methane released from wetlands: implications for the increase in atmospheric methane
Global Biogeochemical Cycles, 2, pp385-397

RAISWELL, R. (1988)
Chemical model for the origin of minor limestone-shale cycles by anaerobic methane oxidation
Geology, 16, pp641-644

RAYBOULD, J.G. AND ANDERSON, D.J. (1987)
Migration of landfill gas and its control by grouting − a case history
Quarterly Journal of Engineering Geology, London, 20, pp75-83

REEBURGH, W.S. (1976)
Methane consumption in Cariaco Trench waters and sediments
Earth and Planetary Science Letters, 28, pp337-344

REEBURGH, W.S. (1980)
Anaerobic methane oxidation: rate depth distributions in Skan Bay sediments
Earth and Planetary Science Letters, 47, pp345-352

REEBURGH, W.S. AND HEGGIE, D.T. (1977)
Microbial methane consumption reactions and their effect on methane distributions in
freshwater and marine environments
Limnology and Oceanography, 22, pp1-9

RICE, D.D. AND CLAYPOOL, G.E. (1981)
Generation, accumulation and resource potential of biogenic gas
Bulletin of the American Association of Petroleum Geologists, 65, pp5-25

RIDLEY, I. AND DOMINIC, K. (1988)
Gas hydrates keep energy on ice
New Scientist, February, pp53-58

ROEDDER, E. (1984)
Fluid Inclusions
Reviews of Mineralogy, Volume 12. Mineralogical Society of America, Washington, D.C.,
USA, 644 pp

ROSHOFF, K. (1989)
Seismic effects on bedrock and underground constructions
A literature survey of damage on constructions; changes in groundwater levels and flow;
changes in chemistry in groundwater and gases
Swedish Nuclear Fuel and Waste Management

SCHOELL, M. (1980)
The hydrogen and carbon isotopic composition of methane from natural gases of various
origins
Geochimica et Cosmochimica Acta, 44, pp649-661

SCHOELL, M. (1983)
Genetic characterisation of natural gases
Bulletin of the American Association of Petroleum Geologists, 67, pp2225-2238

SCHOELL, M. (1988)
Multiple origins of methane in the Earth
In: *Origins of Methane in the Earth* (Guest Ed. M. Schoell)
Chemical Geology, 71, pp1-10

SCHOELL, M., TIETZE, K. AND SCHOBERTH, S.M. (1988)
Origin of methane in Lake Kivu (East-Central Africa)
In: *Origins of Methane in the Earth* (Guest Ed. M. Schoell)
Chemical Geology, 71, pp257-265

SENIOR, E. (Ed.) (1990)
Microbiology of Landfill Sites
CRC Press, Inc., Boca Raton, Florida

SETSCHENOW, A. (1889)
Z. Phys. Chem., 4, 117

SHARP, D.W.A. (1987)
The Penguin Dictionary of Chemistry
Penguin Books

SHEPHERD, T.J., RANKIN, A.H. AND ALDERTON, D.H.M. (1985)
A Practical Guide to Fluid Inclusion Studies
Blackie

SHEPPARD, D.S. AND LYON, G.L. (1984)
Geothermal fluid of the Orakeikorako field, New Zealand
Journal of Volcanology and Geothermal Research, 22, pp329-349

SHERWOOD, B., FRITZ, P., FRAPE, S.K., MACKO, S.A., WEISE, S.M. AND
WELHAN, J.A. (1988)
Methane occurrences in the Canadian Shield
In: *Origins of Methane in the Earth* (Guest Ed. M. Schoell)
Chemical Geology, 71, pp223-236

SHERWOOD LOLLAR, B., FRAPE, S.K., DRIMMIE, R., FRITZ, P., WEISE, S.M.,
MACKO, S.A., WELHAN, J.A., BLOMQVIST, R. AND LAHERMO, P.W. (1989)
Deep gases and brines of the Canadian and Fennoscandian Shields — a testing ground for the
theory of abiotic methane generation
Water-Rock Interaction WRI-6, Proceedings of the 6th Int. Symp., Malvern, UK., D.L. Miles
(Ed), Balkema, Rotterdam, pp617-620

SIMONEIT, B.R.T. (1985)
Hydrothermal petroleum: genesis, migration, and deposition in the Guaymas Basin,
Gulf of California
Canadian Journal of Earth Sciences, 22, pp1919-1929

SIMONEIT, B.R.T., KAWKA, O.E. AND BRAULT, M. (1988)
Origin of gases and condensates in the Guaymas Basin hydrothermal system
(Gulf of California)
In: *Origins of Methane in the Earth* (Guest Ed. M. Schoell)
Chemical Geology, 71, pp169-182

SMITH, A.J. (1988)
Investigation and treatment of gas emissions from abandoned mineworkings
*Proceedings of the Second International Conference on Construction in Areas of Abandoned
Mineworkings*, Edinburgh, 28-30 June, pp205-210

STAFF, M.G. AND SCEAL, J. (1992)
Methane and associated hazards to construction: Research and Information Needs
CIRIA Project Report 5
CIRIA, London

STAFF, M.G., SIZER, K.E. AND NEWSON, S.R. (1991)
The potential for surface emissions of methane from abandoned mine workings
Paper 1.1 Methane — Facing the Problems
Symposium, Nottingham, 26-28 March

STENHOUSE, M.J. AND GROGAN, H. (1991)
Review of reactions of hydrogen and methane in the geosphere and biosphere
Intera Sciences Report No. IG2646-V6 for UK Nirex Ltd. (Nirex Safety Studies Report
No. NSS/R262)

STUMM, W. AND MORGAN, J.J. (1970)
Aquatic Chemistry
John Wiley, New York (Also *ibid* 2nd Edition, 1981)

SUGISAKI, R., ANNO, ADACHI, M. AND UI, H. (1980)
Geochemical features of gases and rocks along active faults
Geochemical Journal, 14, pp101-112

SUGISAKI, R., IDO, M., TAKEDA, H., ISOBE, Y., HAYASHI, Y., NAKAMURA, N., SATAKE, H. AND MIZUTANI, Y. (1983)
Origin of hydrogen and carbon dioxide in fault gases and its relation to fault activity
Journal of Geology, 91, pp239-258

SWAIN, F.M. (1986)
Composition of marsh gases in the central and eastern United States
Applied Geochemistry, 1, pp301-305

SWEENEY, R.E. (1988)
Petroleum-related hydrocarbon seepage in a recent North Sea sediment
Origins of Methane in the Earth (Guest Ed. M. Schoell), *Chemical Geology*, 71, pp53-64

THIMONS, E.D. AND KISSELL, F.N. (1973)
Diffusion of methane through coal
Fuel, 52, pp274-280

TISSOT, B.P. AND WELTE, D.H. (1978)
Petroleum Formation and Occurrence
Springer-Verlag, Berlin

TOMLINSON, M.J. (1988)
Migration of gases through argillaceous rocks, a literature review
Nirex Safety Studies Report No. NSS/R146, UK Nirex Ltd

VAN DEN KERKHOF, A.M. (1988)
The System CO_2-CH_4-N_2: Theoretical Modelling and Geological Applications
Free University Press, Amsterdam

WARREN, C.D., BIRCH, G.P., CROZIER, A. AND EDWARDS, J.S. (1989)
Methane studies for the Channel Tunnel
Paper 4.4 Methane - Facing the Problems
Symposium, Nottingham, 26-28 September (See also Warren, C.D., Birch, G.P., Bennett, A. and Varley, P.M. (1991). Methane studies for the Channel Tunnel *Q.J. Eng. Geol.*, 24, pp291-309)

WELHAN, J.A. (1988)
Origins of methane in hydrothermal systems
Origins of Methane in the Earth (Guest Ed. M. Schoell), *Chemical Geology*, 71, pp183-198

WELHAN, J.A. AND LUPTON, J.E. (1987)
Light hydrocarbon gases in Guaymas Basin hydrothermal fluids: thermogenic versus abiogenic origin
Bulletin of the American Association of Petroleum Geologists, 71, pp215-223

WILHELM, E., BATTINO, R. AND WILCOCK, R.J. (1977)
Low-pressure solubility of gases in liquid water
Chemical Reviews, 77, pp219-262

WILLIAMS, G.M. (1988)
Integrated studies into groundwater pollution by hazardous waste
In: *Land Disposal of Hazardous Waste: Engineering and Environmental Issues* (Eds. J.R. Gronow, A.N. Schofield and R.K. Jain)
Ellis Horwood, Chichester

WILLIAMS, G.M. AND HARRISON I.B. (1983)
Case study of a containment site: the Hooton Landfill, Cheshire
Rep. Brit. Geol. Surv., Fluid Processes Research Group, FLPU 83−8

WILLIAMS, G.M. AND HITCHMAN, S.P. (1989)
The generation and migration of gases in the subsurface
Paper 2.1 Methane — Facing the Problems
Symposium, Nottingham, 26-28 September

WILLIAMS, G.M. AND AITKENHEAD, N. (1989)
The gas explosion at Loscoe, Derbyshire
Paper 3.6 Methane — Facing the Problems
Symposium, Nottingham, 26-28 September

WILLIAMS, G.M. AND AITKENHEAD, N. (1991)
Lessons from Loscoe: the uncontrolled migration of landfill gas
Quarterly Journal of Engineering Geology, 24, pp191-207

WILLIAMSON, I.A. (1991)
Methane, some potential British source rocks
Paper 1.3 Methane — Facing the Problems
Symposium, Nottingham, 26-28 March

WOLFE, R.S. AND HIGGINS I.J. (1979)
Microbial biochemistry of methane — a study in contrasts
Microbial Biochemistry, International Review of Biochemistry, 21, pp267-353

WOLMAN, M.G. (1990)
The impact of man
Eos, Transactions of the American Geophysical Union, 71, pp1884-1886

WRIGHT, V.P. AND VANSTONE, S.D. (1991)
Assessing the carbon dioxide content of ancient atmospheres using palaeocalcretes: theoretical and empirical constraints
J. Geol. Soc., London, 148, pp945-947

WYLLIE, M.R.J. AND SPANGLER, M.B. (1952)
Application of electrical resistivity measurements to problems of fluid flow in porous media.
Bulletin of the American Association of Petroleum Geologists, February, p359

YAMAMOTO, S., ALCAUSKAS, J.B. AND CROZIER, T.E. (1976)
Solubility of methane in distilled water and seawater
J. Chem. Eng. Data, 23, pp69-72

YOUNG, A. (1991)
The influence of weather conditions on landfill gas measurements
(Abstract), Seminar on 'Research relating to certificates of completion'
Envirotrain, Warwickshire, UK

ZOBELL, C.E. (1964)
Geochemical aspects of the microbial modification of carbon compounds
In: *International Series of Monographs on Earth Sciences — Advances in Organic Geochemistry* (Eds. U. Columbo and G.D. Hobson)
Pergamon Press, pp339-356

ZYAKUN, A.M., BONDAR', V.A. AND NAMSARAYEV, B.B. (1979)
Carbon-isotope fraction in microbiological oxidation of methane
Geochemistry International, Vol. 16, No. 1, pp164-169

ZYAKUN, A.M., BONDAR', V.A. AND NAMSARAYEV, B.B. (1986)
Carbon isotope fractionation by methane-oxidizing bacteria
Geochemistry International, 23, 84—90